Microsomal Particles and Protein Synthesis

Papers presented at the First Symposium of the Biophysical Society, at the Massachusetts Institute of Technology, Cambridge, February 5, 6, and 8, 1958

1st SYMPOSIUM
Biophysical Society

Microsomal Particles and Protein Synthesis

RICHARD B. ROBERTS, Editor

Published on behalf
of the
WASHINGTON ACADEMY OF SCIENCES
WASHINGTON, D. C.

by

PERGAMON PRESS
NEW YORK • *LONDON* • *PARIS* • *LOS ANGELES*
1958

© *Richard B. Roberts 1958*

Library of Congress Catalog Card Number 58-13658

THE LORD BALTIMORE PRESS, INC.

FOREWORD

The formation of a new society provides an occasion for innovations in the forms of meetings and publications. The Program Committee of the Biophysical Society attempted to seize this opportunity in arranging the 1958 meeting at Cambridge. In addition to the usual short contributed papers, review papers were scheduled for the three afternoon sessions to inform the membership of progress and problems in selected areas of biophysics. The contributed papers in these areas were allocated ample time for presentation and discussion, resulting in what might be called "contributed symposia." Those working in the field had the advantages of a symposium type of meeting; those less familiar had an introduction provided by the review papers followed by an opportunity to participate in the detailed technical sessions.

It also appeared desirable to alter the usual publication procedures. Customarily the complete proceedings of "invited symposia" are published but only the abstracts of short contributions. The twenty papers dealing with microsomal particles normally would be published individually during the next two years, scattered through different issues of five or ten journals. Alternatively, it would be possible to publish a transcript of the symposium. This procedure would provide a more complete account than is given in the abstracts; the material would be in one volume; and it could be issued much more rapidly than individual contributions to journals. Both the Council of the Biophysical Society and a majority of the contributors favored publication of the symposium material.

Transcripts, however, require an enormous editorial effort. It therefore seemed preferable to request the contributors to provide their own edited transcripts. These transcripts have been accepted with the understanding that publication in this volume which records material presented at a meeting would not preclude later publication in the usual journals.

The purpose of this volume is not to present well established theories or reviews of well known work. Rather, it is to publish new facts and new data while they are still fresh, useful, and possibly wrong. The relative costs of research time and publication make such a book worth purchasing if it saves no more than an hour of research time. The entire publication costs are justified if the book can save a month in some research program.

v

The Washington Academy of Sciences has agreed to act as publisher in the hope of demonstrating that this type of book can be brought out rapidly and that it does serve a useful function.

We wish to thank the Office of Publications of Carnegie Institution of Washington for editorial help in seeing the project through the press.

D. B. COWIE
Chairman, Monograph Committee
Washington Academy of Sciences

C. LEVINTHAL
Chairman, Program Committee
Biophysical Society

R. B. ROBERTS, *Editor*
Carnegie Institution of Washington
Department of Terrestrial Magnetism
5241 Broad Branch Road, Northwest
Washington 15, D. C.

INTRODUCTION

The topic "Microsomal Particles and Protein Synthesis" seemed particularly appropriate for the first symposium of the Biophysical Society. The particles owe their recognition to the electron microscope and the ultracentrifuge. X-ray diffraction studies will undoubtedly contribute to the picture of the structure of the particles; radioactive tracers show the kinetics of formation of the particles and their products; radiation experiments can give other evidence about the role of the particles in protein synthesis. Thus many of the special areas of competence of biophysicists are involved in the study of the particles.

More important, however, is the timeliness of a symposium devoted to a discussion of these ubiquitous granules. For a number of years circumstantial evidence has accumulated which indicates that ribonucleic acid (RNA) is implicated in protein synthesis. More recently it has been recognized that a large part of the RNA occurs in the form of ribonucleoprotein (RNP) particles. Particles of roughly the same size and composition have been isolated from sources differing as widely as rat liver, pea seedlings, and microorganisms. Accordingly there has developed a widespread faith that the particles are an important part of the machinery for protein synthesis.

It must be admitted, however, that the evidence is entirely circumstantial. A number of arguments would come immediately to the mind of a lawyer defending the particles from the charge of protein synthesis. (1) In vivo experiments have shown incorporation of radioactive tracers which is initially higher in the microsome fraction than in the soluble proteins, but the kinetic data are not sufficiently complete to prove a precursor-product relationship. For example, it is possible that steady-state conditions do not prevail; there is no certainty that both components draw on the same pool of amino acids; only the average of the soluble proteins is measured, whereas individual components might behave quite differently. (2) There are many cases both in complete and in cell-free systems where RNAase has been observed to inhibit protein synthesis. In many of these the addition of RNA (*not* RNP) is sufficient to restore the synthetic activity. (3) Cell-free systems showing unequivocal protein synthesis use cells that are only partially disrupted, and the requirement for particles is not demonstrated. In those systems where the particles have been partly purified, the incorporation data are more suggestive of exchange than of true protein synthesis. (4) No mechanism has been suggested which shows how the structure of the particle is compatible with its function as the template for synthesis of long chains. It appears that the particles have not yet been proved guilty beyond all reasonable doubt. In the last few years, however, there have been marked advances in the study of the particles which promise to resolve these lingering doubts. Thus a symposium dealing with the particles and their function in living cells could hardly fail to bring forth new and exciting information.

In this symposium a number of papers were concerned with methods of isolation, the size, the composition, and the stability of the particles. One striking observation was that particles of roughly 80 S are found in a wide variety of materials; another area of agreement was in the requirement for magnesium to stabilize the particles. There was a consensus of opinion that carefully purified particles have little enzymatic activity and that their RNA content is 40 per cent or more. Several reports showed that the protein moieties of nucleoprotein have certain distinctive properties. Other studies explored the reasons for the variations in particle sizes that are observed both in vivo and in vitro. New kinetic data were presented which indicate that the protein of the particles does not serve as precursor material for nonparticulate protein. The incorporation of adenylamino acids was demonstrated in one study which also illuminated the need for caution in the interpretation of incorporation studies. Other papers reported less direct methods of approach to the understanding of the particles and their role in protein synthesis, such as studies of radiation effects and studies of incorporation of amino acid analogs. All together these reports provide a number of new facts that must be taken into account by any theory of protein and nucleic acid synthesis.

During the course of the symposium a semantic difficulty became apparent. To some of the participants, microsomes mean the ribonucleoprotein particles of the microsome fraction contaminated by other protein and lipid material; to others, the microsomes consist of protein and lipid contaminated by particles. The phrase "microsomal particles" does not seem adequate, and "ribonucleoprotein particles of the microsome fraction" is much too awkward. During the meeting the word "ribosome" was suggested; this seems a very satisfactory name, and it has a pleasant sound. The present confusion would be eliminated if "ribosome" were adopted to designate ribonucleoprotein particles in the size range 20 to 100 S.

The symposium provided to the participants an opportunity for comparing notes on methods and techniques and for exchange of views on the status of various problems. It undoubtedly affected the immediate research plans of a number of the participants. This volume is being published in the hope that it will extend some of these benefits to those who did not attend.

CONTENTS

1

Isolation and Characterization
of Bacterial Nucleoprotein Particles

WILLIAM C. GILLCHRIEST   ROBERT M. BOCK

Department of Biochemistry, University of Wisconsin

Fractionation of the particulate matter from broken cells has long excited the biochemist. Lilienfeld [1] prepared nuclear and cytoplasmic fractions and studied the properties of a deoxynucleoprotein (DNP). Huiskamp [2] noted the influence of buffer salts on isolated DNP. The possibility of differential extraction of subcellular structures was investigated by Bensley and Hoerr [3]. The technique of purifying subcellular components has advanced rapidly through the efforts of Claude [4], Hogeboom and Schneider [5], and Anderson [6].

The fractionation of subcellular components offers the possibility of integrating the fields of intracellular anatomy, cellular physiology, and biochemistry. Siekevitz [7] working with mitochondria and Palade [8] and Zamecnik [9] working with the microsomal fraction have begun this integration by equating isolated fractions to structures observed in the electron microscope. Our studies with the ribonucleoprotein of *Azotobacter vinelandii* have clearly demonstrated that progress in this integration of fields demands a detailed understanding of the properties and stability of the subcellular particles. Previous studies [10] on the protein synthesis in cell-free extracts of *A. vinelandii* must now be reinterpreted in the light of our current understanding of the stability of bacterial ribonucleoprotein.

In 1954 Palade and Porter [8a] demonstrated endoplasmic reticulum in animal cells. Hodge, Martin, and Morton [11] in 1957 demonstrated similar structures in plant cells, and Sacks [12] has found related structures in yeasts, higher molds, and algae, leaving, at the present time, only the bacteria without clearly demonstrated endoplasmic reticulum. Pochon [13] found structures in *A. vinelandii* which by staining and observation in the light microscope were identified as nuclei. We have observed granularity in regions of thin sections through

A. vinelandii examined in the electron microscope. Several speakers at this conference have referred to similar granularity in sections of *Escherichia coli* as ribonucleoprotein particles, but no clear identification of these granules as such has yet been accomplished. Ribonucleoprotein particles, similar in size and chemical composition to those from animal cells, yeast, and fungi [14], can, however, be prepared from bacteria [15]. Several papers in this volume describe the ribonucleoprotein of *E. coli,* and this paper will treat the preparation and properties of ribonucleoprotein particles from *A. vinelandii.*

RUPTURE OF BACTERIAL CELLS

One of the aims of this work is to prepare subcellular structures having a useful correspondence to structures that existed in the intact cell. We have no single criterion to indicate when such a preparation has been accomplished, but we use as supporting evidence reproducibility of the product when prepared by several varying methods and we also invoke all the information about the stability of isolated components. The stability observations are described in a later section of this paper. Three different methods of cell rupture have been found to permit isolation of indistinguishable particles, provided that the cultures used were harvested at a similar stage of growth.

The first method was physical grinding with number 320 mesh Carborundum which had been washed with hydrochloric acid and rinsed with distilled water until neutral. The cells had been previously washed with distilled water. The packed cell paste was ground with 4 parts by weight Carborundum for approximately 15 minutes or until moist. An additional 2 parts of Carborundum was added, and the cells were ground for approximately 5 minutes more. Visible microscopic examination of the mixture revealed that approximately 95 per cent of the cells were ruptured by the grinding method. The ground cells were diluted with 8 times the original cell volume of the following buffer: 1.6×10^{-3} M K_2HPO_4, 0.4×10^{-3} M KH_2PO_4, and 5×10^{-3} M $MgSO_4$. This will be referred to as the RNP buffer. The supernate from centrifuging this mixture at $500g$ for 30 minutes is referred to as the crude extract.

The second method of cell breakage employed cells grown in the presence of 2 M glycerol. The cells were collected by low-speed centrifugation, and the pellet was diluted into 8 volumes of the RNP buffer to rupture and produce the crude extract.

In the third method of cell breakage, *A. vinelandii* protoplasts were ruptured by osmotic shock. Weibull [16] showed that *Bacillus megatherium,* when treated with lysozyme in sucrose solutions of high osmotic pressure, changed to a spherical form which is readily ruptured by lowering the osmotic pressure. We have avoided the use of sucrose in view of our findings on the instability of the isolated particles in dilute sucrose solutions. The *A. vinelandii* cells were washed in the RNP buffer, and suspended in 1.5×10^{-3} M EDTA at a dilution such that the optical density at 660 mμ was approximately 0.75. These solutions had been previously osmotically adjusted with glycerol or with Carbowax "4000" to maintain the protoplasts. The turbid solutions were brought to 13 µg/ml in crystalline egg white lysozyme, and the turbidity was observed until its rapid decrease ceased. The protoplasts were then collected by low-speed centrifugation, washed once in osmotically adjusted RNP buffer, collected again, and ruptured by osmotic shock upon dilution with 10 times the packed cell volume of RNP buffer to yield a crude extract. During the development of the protoplast procedure, both the formation of the protoplasts and their osmotic rupture upon dilution were followed in the visible and phase contrast microscope.

PURIFICATION OF RIBONUCLEOPROTEIN PARTICLES (fig. 1)

The crude extract derived from any of the above three procedures is centrifuged at 4900g for 30 minutes. The pellet that accumulates consists of cell debris

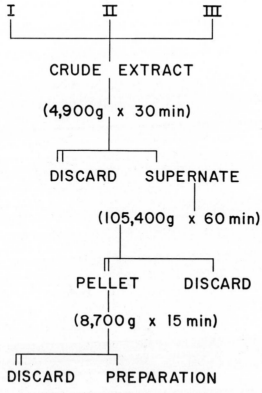

Fig. 1. Flow sheet for differential centrifugation of ribonucleoprotein from a crude extract of *A. vinelandii* prepared by I grinding, II osmotic shock, or III protoplastic osmotic shock.

and, with method I, some Carborundum that was not removed at lower speeds. The supernatant liquid from this step is now centrifuged at 105,000g for 60 minutes. The pellet so obtained is solubilized in RNP buffer for approximately 12 hours, and then centrifuged at 8700g for 15 minutes. The precipitate is discarded, and the supernatant liquid is examined in the analytical ultracentrifuge to determine the number of sedimenting components, their relative amounts, and their sedimentation coefficients. When the 86 S component is desired, the 105,000g and the 8700g cycle is repeated until over 90 per cent of the area in the schlieren pattern is under the appropriate peak.

PROPERTIES OF RIBONUCLEOPROTEIN PARTICLES

When a crude extract is processed to the stage labeled "preparation" in figure 1, and is examined in the analytical ultracentrifuge, it is found to sediment as a single peak of sedimentation coefficient 86 S. If, however, the same crude extract is carried to the same stage employing a buffer in which the magnesium concentration has been reduced to 10^{-3} M, the ultracentrifuge pattern now shows five significant components. Comparison of the schlieren and ultraviolet absorption photographs in the ultracentrifuge suggests that all these components contain nucleoprotein. The sedimentation coefficients extrapolated to zero concentration and corrected to 20° C are 86, 77, 58, 39, and 10 S. The 86, 58, and 39 S components are usually found in largest amount. Figures 2 and 3

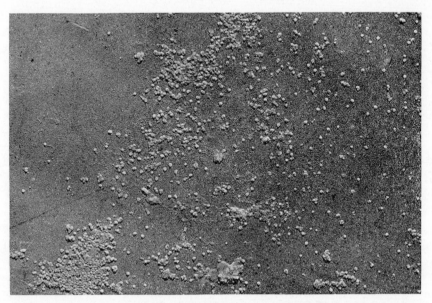

Fig. 2. An electron micrograph of the edge of a droplet of RNP particles sprayed onto a collodion membrane and shadowed with uranium. Magnified 34,000 times. Taken on a Siemens Elmiskop I by Professor Paul Kaesberg.

Fig. 3. An electron micrograph of a central portion of a sprayed droplet showing RNP particles magnified 170,000 times. The smallest particles are about 200 A in diameter, the largest about 250 A. From the shapes of their shadows it is estimated that their thicknesses are about 75 per cent as great as their diameters. Taken on a Siemens Elmiskop I by Professor Paul Kaesberg.

are electron micrographs of a purified preparation of the 86 S particles which was diluted 1000fold with distilled water and then quickly sprayed on a collodion membrane and air-dried. It is not yet known how the short exposure to distilled water will affect particle structure. The electron micrographs taken under these conditions show that at least two size classes are present, both of which are roughly spherical. The 86, 58, and 39 S particles all show small dependence of sedimentation coefficient on concentration, which also suggests that the particles are not markedly asymmetric.

The particles appear to contain ribonucleic acid and protein and to be free of lipid and deoxynucleic acid. The nucleic acid component has been separated and purified by detergent treatment [17], phenol [18], chloroform [19], and glacial acetic acid [20] extraction. The protein component when separated from the nucleic acid has been found to be insoluble in aqueous solutions unless prepared through a 67 per cent glacial acetic acid procedure. The protein shows an ultraviolet absorption typical of a protein rich in tyrosine. We have derived only one major protein from the particle at this point. The derived protein appears to have only one type of N-terminal amino acid, which we have very tentatively identified as glycine. The number of protein subunits per particle has not yet been quantitatively determined, but the experiments to date suggest a large number.

Ribose nucleic acid prepared from the particle by chloroform extraction of the protein shows markedly the hyperchromic effect characteristic of polymerized nucleic acids. Immediately upon addition of the alkali the optical density at 260 mμ increases 15 per cent. After incubation for 16 hours at 30° C with 0.5 N NaOH and adjusting the pH to 7.5, the final hyperchromic effect is found to be 39.1 per cent. The nucleotides (table 1) arising upon alkaline hydrolysis of the ribose nucleic acid have been chromatographed on Dowex-l-formate ion-exchange columns developed with gradient elution. The unknown nucleotide shows chromatographic behavior similar to that of the new ribonucleotide reported by Cohn, but its acid, alkaline, and neutral ultraviolet absorption spectra are not identical to those of the fifth nucleotide which we have isolated from yeast.

The 86 S particle has been examined for its stability as a function of salt, chelating agents, enzymatic attack, pH, and sucrose concentration (fig. 4). The results of these studies were fed back into improvements in the preparative procedure and are of utmost importance to the interpretation of labeled amino acid incorporation studies in the particulate fractions of *A. vinelandii*. If the 86 S particle is suspended in a pH 7.05 buffer of 2×10^{-3} M phosphate, 10^{-3} M $MgSO_4$, with NaCl added to a total ionic strength of 0.03, or is dialyzed against 2×10^{-3} M $K_2HPO_4:KH_2PO_4$ (4:1) buffer, it dissociates to yield 58 and 39 S components.

Our early studies showed that the 58 and 39 S components could be returned to 10^{-3} M Mg^{++}–containing solutions without re-forming the 86 S particle which had previously been stable to that environment. Encouraged by our discussions with Dr. Paul Ts'o at this conference, we explored further and found that in 5×10^{-3} M Mg^{++} the 58 and 39 S components recombined to form the 86 S particle, and that once formed this particle again was stable in 10^{-3} Mg^{++}. In all these studies the buffer also contained 2×10^{-3} M potassium phosphate buffer of pH 7.05.[1] We also confirm Ts'o's observation that the area of the 39 S peak is about one-half that of the 58 S peak, which suggests that one small 39 S and one larger 58 S particle combine to form the 86 S particle. Upon addition of 0.01 M, pH 7, ethylenediaminetetraacetic acid, the particles further dissociated to ribonucleoprotein of sedimentation coefficient less than 5 S (not extrapolated to zero concentration). The particles are also rapidly degraded to small fragments by ribonuclease but are not attacked by deoxyribonuclease. They are precipitated by pH below 6.5 or above 7.5.

Attempts to use sucrose for certain stages of the purification led to the observation that, if sucrose was added to the RNP buffer, the particles aggregated and were readily removed by low-speed centrifugation. Sucrose concentrations from 3 to 30 per cent were all found to have this effect. This finding necessi-

---

[1] *Note added in proof:* We recently reported at the 1958 meeting of the Federation of American Societies for Experimental Biology that a buffer 5×10^{-3} M in MgO and adjusted to pH 7.05 with cacodylic acid gives improved yield and excellent stability of the 80 S class of RNP from yeast, *E. coli*, and *A. vinelandii*.

TABLE 1. Analysis of Nucleic Acid Hydrolyzed with 0.5 N NaOH
for 16 Hours at 37° C

Hydrolyzate was chromatographed on a Dowex-1-formate column with gradient elution.

	Nucleoprotein Particle, mole %	Whole Cells,* mole %
AMP	25	24
GMP	24	31
CMP	19	26
UMP	24	20
Unknown nucleotide	7	Not reported

* Whole cell data from Lombard and Chargaff [21].

tates re-evaluation of some studies [10] that have been carried out on *A. vine-landii* and raises the important question whether this phenomenon can occur in ribonucleoprotein from other sources.

The ribonucleoprotein has been assayed for a large number of enzymatic activities. It appears free of nucleotide phosphatase activity, glucose-1-phosphatase, oxidative phosphorylation enzymes, and electron-transport enzymes. A feeble glucose-6-phosphatase activity of 10 mM phosphate released per minute

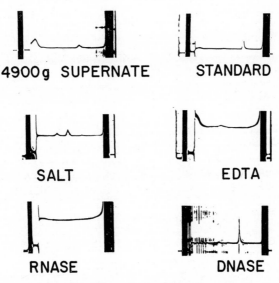

Fig. 4. The preparation and stability of *A. vinelandii* nucleoprotein. Each analytical ultracentrifuge pattern is labeled with the stage of preparation (top pair) or the treatment to which a pure 86 S product was subjected. The salt and EDTA treatment are described in the text. The RNAse action occurred in less than 5 minutes at 1 part of enzyme per 1000 parts of particle whereas the DNAse at the same concentration produced no change in 45 minutes.

per gram of particle was detected, but it is at most a few per cent of that found in equal weights of liver microsome fractions.

DISCUSSION

The study of *A. vinelandii* ribonucleoprotein has been more successful in posing interesting questions than in providing answers to previous questions. Can the sharp requirements of the nucleoprotein for divalent cations and for certain *p*H ranges be exploited to give information on the mode of combination of nucleic acid and protein or combination between nucleoprotein subunits? Does the marked difference in ribonuclease sensitivity of the plant ribonucleoprotein viruses and the bacterial ribonucleoprotein imply a different orientation or localization of nucleic acid and protein? The plant viruses now appear to have a protein coating with nucleic acid (or nucleoprotein) in an inner layer concentric with the protein coat and thus protected from ribonuclease attack. How different must the structure be to permit the rapid attack observed?

Will the small subunits derivable by salt and EDTA treatment also yield information on the mode of action or size of the functional nucleic acid?

The striking effect of divalent cations on the physical state of nucleoprotein is now becoming recognized as a phenomenon common to many systems. Huiskamp [2] in 1901 noted that thymus nucleoprotein was precipitated by 0.01 *M* calcium, barium, and magnesium salts and dissolved in excesses (0.1 *M*) of these same salts. He equated changes in physical properties of nucleoprotein solutions during dialysis to losses of divalent cations. He noted that heavy-metal divalent cations formed nucleoprotein precipitates that were difficult to dissolve. Korkes [22] and co-workers used a similar observation on manganese RNP to remove RNP from bacterial extracts. Carter and Hall [23] working in the laboratories of J. W. Williams noted that thymus nucleoprotein in sodium chloride solutions was a rodlike molecule but in calcium chloride solutions it became compact and showed no dependence of sedimentation rate on concentration. Wiberg and Neuman [24] have studied the binding of magnesium and calcium by RNA and DNA and find a region of concentration through which the number of equivalents bound changes rapidly. This concentration range is the same as that which we find critical for nucleoprotein structural changes.

The studies reported here, added to the work of Mazia [25] on the role of polyvalent cations in deoxynucleoprotein and nuclear structure and of Chao and Schachman [14*a*] in ribonucleoprotein stability, and to the many excellent contributions presented at the second annual Biophysics Conference, will help establish the basic rules for fractionation of subcellular particles in a reproducible manner.

The dependence of nucleoprotein structure upon divalent cation concentration is striking enough for these ions to become of interest in consideration of the variables which dictate when a nucleic acid will be in the double helix, when it will split, when it is "soluble RNA," and when not. Re-evaluation of Brachet's [26] findings on the relation of ribonucleoprotein to growth phase of yeast will be warranted in the light of current concepts of the importance of buffer media.

Whereas the divalent cations of the buffer medium play an important role in nucleoprotein structure, there appear to be mineral elements which are influential in nucleic acid function and are not in free equilibrium with the buffer. Zittle [27] and Jungner [28] demonstrated that carefully isolated yeast RNA contained characteristic amounts of metal ions. Kihlman [29] and Mazia [25] have related structural integrity of chromosomes to metal content. Loring and Cooper [30] find that certain cations are important for nucleoprotein stability of tobacco mosaic virus and hence for infectivity. Racker and Krimsky [31] have evidence that metal ions are involved in an animal virus. These are but a few of the many nucleoprotein-metal systems cited in the literature.

Thus it appears that for viruses, as well as for subcellular particles, elucidation of the structural and functional role of cations will be a fertile and challenging frontier for those with pioneering instincts.

SUMMARY

Ribonucleoprotein particles of sedimentation coefficient $S_{20^\circ} = 86$ have been isolated from *A. vinelandii*. The particles are free of lipid and DNA. They are stable at neutral pH, in low-ionic-strength solution when divalent cations are present; they are unstable in sucrose, in concentrated salts, and in the presence of ribonuclease. Nucleic acid derived from the particles contains an unidentified fifth base. The 86 S unit reversibly dissociates to particles of 58 and 39 S when the Mg^{++} concentration is lowered.

ACKNOWLEDGMENTS

We are pleased to acknowledge the generous aid of our colleagues. Professor Paul Kaesberg conducted the electron-microscope studies, Miss Vatsala Thakur provided the N-terminal amino acid analyses, and Miss Fay Hoh collaborated in studies on the protein derived from the particles. Financial support from the National Institutes of Health and Wisconsin Alumni Research Foundation is gratefully acknowledged.

REFERENCES

1. L. Lilienfeld, *Z. physiol. Chem.*, *18*, 473 (1894).

2. W. Huiskamp, *Z. physiol. Chem.*, *32*, 145 (1901).

3. R. R. Bensley and N. L. Hoerr, *Anat. Record*, *60*, 251 (1934).

4a. A. Claude, *Harvey Lectures*, *43*, 121 (1948).

4b. A. Claude, *Advances in Protein Chem.*, *5*, 423 (1949).

5. W. C. Schneider and G. H. Hogeboom, *J. Biol. Chem. 183*, 123 (1950).

6. N. G. Anderson, *Science, 121*, 775 (1955).

7. P. Siekevitz and M. L. Watson, *J. Biophys. Biochem. Cytol.*, 2, no. 6, 653 (1956).

8a. G. E. Palade and K. R. Porter, *J. Exptl. Med., 100,* 641 (1954).

8b. G. E. Palade, *J. Biophys. Biochem. Cytol., 2,* 547 (1954).

8c. G. E. Palade and K. L. Porter, *J. Biophys. Biochem. Cytol., 3,* 269 (1957).

8d. G. E. Palade, *J. Biophys. Biochem. Cytol., 2,* no. 4, Suppl., 85 (1956).

8e. G. E. Palade and P. Siekevitz, *J. Biophys. Biochem. Cytol., 2,* 171 (1956).

9. P. C. Zamecnik, *Sci. American, 3,* 118 (1958).

10. D. P. Burma and R. H. Burris, *J. Biol. Chem., 225,* 287 (1957).

11. A. J. Hodge, E. M. Martin, and R. K. Morton, *J. Biophys. Biochem. Cytol., 3,* no. 1, 61 (1957).

12. Irving B. Sacks, personal communication.

13. J. Pochon, Y. T. Tchan, and T. L. Wang, *Ann. inst. Pasteur, 74,* 182 (1948).

14a. Fu-Chuan Chao and H. K. Schachman, *Arch. Biochem. Biophys., 61,* 220 (1956).

14b. Fu-Chuan Chao, *Arch. Biochem. Biophys., 70,* 426 (1957).

15. H. K. Schachman, A. B. Pardee, and R. Y. Stanier, *Arch. Biochem. Biophys., 38,* 245 (1952).

16. C. Weibull, *J. Bacteriol., 66,* 688 (1953).

17. E. R. M. Kay and A. L. Dounce, *J. Am. Chem. Soc., 75,* 4041 (1953).

18. G. Schramm, *A Symposium on the Chemical Basis of Heredity* (W. D. McElroy and Bentley Glass, eds.), p. 513, 1957.

19. M. G. Sevag, D. B. Lackman, and J. Smolena, *J. Biol. Chem., 124,* 425 (1938).

20. H. Fraenkel-Conrat, *Virology, 4,* 1–4 (1957).

21. A. Lombard and E. Chargaff, *Biochim. et Biophys. Acta, 20,* 285 (1956).

22. S. Korkes, A. del Campino, I. C. Gunsales, and S. Ochoa, *J. Biol. Chem., 193,* 721 (1951).

23. R. O. Carter and J. L. Hall, *Nature, 144,* 329 (1939).

24. J. S. Wiberg and W. F. Neuman, *Arch. Biochem. Biophys., 72,* 66 (1957).

25. D. Mazia, *Proc. Natl. Acad. Sci. U. S., 40,* 521 (1954).

26. J. Brachet and R. Jener, *Bieres et boissons, 3,* 422 (1942).

27. C. A. Zittle, *J. Biol. Chem., 163,* 111 (1946).

28. G. Jungner, *Science, 113,* 378 (1951).

29. B. A. Kihlman, *J. Biophys. Biochem. Cytol., 3,* 363, 381 (1957).

30. H. S. Loring and W. D. Cooper, *J. Biol. Chem., 211,* 505 (1956).

31. E. Racker and I. Krimsky, *J. Exptl. Med., 85,* 715 (1945).

2

The Stabilization and Physical Characteristics of Purified Bacterial Ribonucleoprotein Particles

JACK WAGMAN   WESTON R. TRAWICK

U. S. Army Chemical Corps, Fort Detrick, Frederick, Maryland

Principally through electron-microscope studies on thin sections of various species [1] it has been possible to show that a major part of the bacterial cytoplasm consists of widely dispersed granules 100 to 200 A in diameter. In ultracentrifugal analysis of aqueous extracts from disrupted bacteria, Schachman, Pardee, and Stanier [2] found one of the major components, with $s_{20,w} = 40$ S, to consist of roughly spherical particles, about 150 A in diameter, which contain much of the cytoplasmic ribonucleic acid (RNA). A variety of enzymatic functions have since been attributed to these particles [3], including the systems for electron transport, for oxidative phosphorylation, and for some of the reactions of the tricarboxylic acid cycle.

The present paper reports attempts to isolate the 40 S component, by successive differential centrifugation of extracts from *Escherichia coli,* and physical measurements obtained with purified material. Particular attention is drawn to the observation that the stability of these particles is dependent upon a dialyzable substance in cell extracts which apparently inhibits decomposition.

MATERIALS AND METHODS

The extracts used were prepared from *E. coli* (ATCC 4157) grown 24 hours on nutrient agar at 37° C. After washing by alternate centrifugation and resuspension, cells were disrupted by shaking with glass beads in a Mickle disintegrator. The procedure consisted of shaking 6-ml volumes of suspensions (about 7×10^{10} cells/ml) with 5 g of beads (type 114 Minnesota Mining and Manufacturing Company) for 5-minute periods at 1700 cycles per minute. The extracts were then cleared of unbroken cells and debris by low-speed centrifugation. Potassium phosphate buffer, pH 7.0 and ionic strength 0.1, was used in the preparation of extracts.

Preparative and analytical sedimentation were carried out in Spinco ultracentrifuges Models L and E, respectively. A diffusion constant measurement was made by free diffusion in a Claesson cell [4]. Partial specific volume was determined by density measurements in a Lipkin pycnometer [5].

RESULTS

Decomposition Inhibitor in E. coli Extracts. It has been shown that the extractive procedure described here yields solutions that are highly reproducible as determined by sedimentation and electrophoretic behavior [6]. The sedimentation diagram (see fig. 1) corresponds closely to those obtained previously [2] by other methods of cell disruption. The rapidly sedimenting 40 S component is clearly resolvable, and it appears that a considerably purified preparation should be obtainable simply by successive differential centrifugation. In early fractionation attempts, pellets from solutions subjected to centrifugal fields about 100,000g for 90 minutes (in the no. 30 rotor of the Model L Spinco) were found to be only partly resoluble, in agreement with the finding of Schachman et al. [2]. Moreover, the soluble material, as shown in figure 1, contained an unexpectedly large amount of more slowly sedimenting material along with a disappointingly low quantity of 40 S component.

In a subsequent study to determine the effect of dialysis on the nature of *E. coli* extracts, an observation was made that proved to be an important step in this purification problem. As shown in figure 2, the 40 S component in dialyzed extracts was greatly reduced in concentration with a simultaneous increase in the quantity of more slowly sedimenting material. In additional experiments, however, the effect was found to be diminished as the dialysate-extract volume ratio was decreased. This suggested the presence, in those extracts, of a dialyzable material that functions as a stabilizer of the 40 S component. A substance with an analogous property has been reported by Petermann and Hamilton [7] in studies with rat liver homogenates.

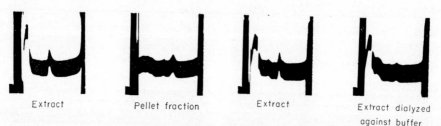

Extract   Pellet fraction   Extract   Extract dialyzed
                                                                            against buffer

Fig. 1. Sedimentation diagrams of an *E. coli* extract and the pellet fraction derived by a two-step centrifugation at 100,000g for 90 minutes. Patterns were recorded 7 minutes after attainment of full field strength, about 250,000g.

Fig. 2. The effect of dialysis on the sedimentation behavior of an extract from *E. coli*. Recording of diagrams took place 8 minutes after full field strength was reached, 250,000g.

The stabilizing effect of the dialyzable material, which is tentatively designated "decomposition inhibitor" (DI), was further demonstrated as follows. After overnight dialysis of 1 volume of extract solution against 4 volumes of water, the dialysate was lyophilized and reconstituted to four-fifths of the volume of extract used. This procedure yields a solution, which we shall refer to as buffer-DI, whose concentration of dialyzable material is roughly equal to that of the original extract. The stabilizing effect of the DI was then observed by comparing the sedimentation behavior of fresh extract solutions dialyzed against buffer and buffer-DI, respectively. As is shown in figure 3, the DI effectively prevented the disappearance of 40 S component.

The nature of the stabilizing substance is not clear. An analysis of the dialyzable material indicates the presence of peptides and nucleotides as well as trace amounts of magnesium, iron, and other metals usually found in bacterial extracts. Metal ions appear to be ruled out as the active substance, for the stabilizing effect is lost by heating the buffer-DI for 5 minutes at about 90° C.

Purification of 40 S Component. It now appears that the early difficulties in fractionating the 40 S component were due to a procedure which separates that component from the stabilizer. By slightly modifying the original fractionation scheme, the 40 S component was prepared in a relatively high state of purity and stability. The pellets, after each of two successive centrifugation steps, were redissolved in previously prepared buffer-DI. Figure 4 shows a comparison of preparations, from a single batch of cells, obtained by this and the previous methods. The sedimentation patterns demonstrate the degree of purity with which it is possible to obtain the 40 S component, and illustrate the activity of the DI.

Physicochemical Properties. An analysis of the fractionated material indicated

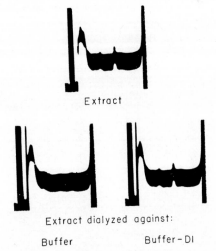

Extract

Extract dialyzed against:

Buffer   Buffer-DI

Fig. 3. Sedimentation diagrams illustrating the protective effect of the dialyzable stabilizer on the 40 S component in *E. coli* extracts.

Crude extract

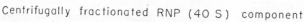
Centrifugally fractionated RNP (40 S) component

Without buffer-DI   Using buffer-DI   Using buffer-DI
observed initially   observed 4 days later

Fig. 4. Sedimentation diagrams illustrating the influence of the stabilizing medium (buffer-DI) on the nature of the RNP fraction obtainable from *E. coli* extracts by differential centrifugation. Diagrams were recorded about 5 minutes after full field strength was reached, 250,000*g*.

that it consisted entirely of protein and ribose nucleic acid in a proportion about 3 to 1 by weight. Since the material appears to be essentially monodisperse, it is tentatively concluded that the 40 S particles contain protein and nucleic acid in combination as a ribonucleoprotein (RNP).

Sedimentation, diffusion, and partial specific volume measurements were carried out with the RNP fraction, the more detailed data being obtained with water as the solvent. The results are summarized in table 1. Although, as is seen in figure 4, very small amounts of more slowly sedimenting material were present in these preparations, they are believed not to cause serious errors in the use of these data to determine particle characteristics.

TABLE 1. Sedimentation and Diffusion Constants of Centrifugally Fractionated Ribonucleoprotein from Extracts of *E. coli*

Preparation	Solvent	Concentration mg/ml	$10^{13}s_{20,w}$ sec	$10^7 D_{20,w}$ cm^2 sec^{-1}	$\bar{V}_{20}$	M	f/f_0
a	0.1 ionic strength phosphate buffer, *p*H 7.0	6.3	45.0	. . .	. . .	. . .	. . .
b	Water	8.0	43.6	2.67	0.657	1,240,000	1.16
		6.0	44.4				
		2.0	46.0				
		0	46.9 *				

* Value obtained by extrapolating $1/s$.

The very slight concentration dependence of $s_{20, w}$ (with a value, at infinite dilution, of 46.9 S) is in agreement with the finding by Schachman et al. [2] that these particles appear to be roughly spherical in the electron microscope. On the assumption of a negligible concentration dependence for diffusion, the molecular weight calculated from the measured data is 1,240,000, and the frictional ratio, f/f_0, is 1.16, corresponding to spheres, 137 A in diameter, hydrated to the extent of 0.37 ml/g of RNP.

An electron micrograph, made using a water solution of RNP, is shown in figure 5. The particles appear to be uniformly spherical with a mean diameter about 152 A. This value is in good agreement with the sedimentation-diffusion figure, inasmuch as the probable errors with the electron microscope tend to yield too high a figure.

DISCUSSION

It has been reported (e.g., by Chao and Schachman [8] and by Bolton, Hoyer, and Ritter, paper 3 of this volume) that more rapidly sedimenting components (60 S and 80 S) appear in extracts from microbial cells when magnesium ions are present in sufficient concentration in the extract media. This addition to the ionic environment is not required for the preservation of the 47 S particles dealt with in the present report. In the intact cell, the synthesis and dissociation of RNP particles are probably controlled by several factors which may include magnesium and other ions. The action of ribonuclease, for example, is inhibited by a large number of substances [9] including bivalent cations and mononucleotides, all of which are apparently present in the dialyzable fraction of *E. coli* extracts.

Although the RNP component has been identified with a variety of enzymatic functions, it is not clear whether these are intrinsic or merely adsorbed. Electrophoretic data [6] show that this material, despite its apparent monodispersity in the ultracentrifuge and electron microscope, is heterogeneous, consisting of two or more components with a wide range of anodic mobilities at pH 7.0.

ACKNOWLEDGMENT

We wish to acknowledge the assistance of Mrs. F. Elizabeth White in the growth and harvesting of the *E. coli* cultures and of Mr. Robert L. Sine in the preparation of the electron micrograph.

SUMMARY

A dialyzable substance in extracts from *E. coli* has been found to inhibit the decomposition of the RNP particles (previously referred to as the 40 S component). This observation has led to the preparation of the RNP fraction in a relatively high state of purity and stability. Physical measurements indicate that the RNP component consists of uniformly spherical particles with a molecular weight 1,240,000 and a diameter of 137 A.

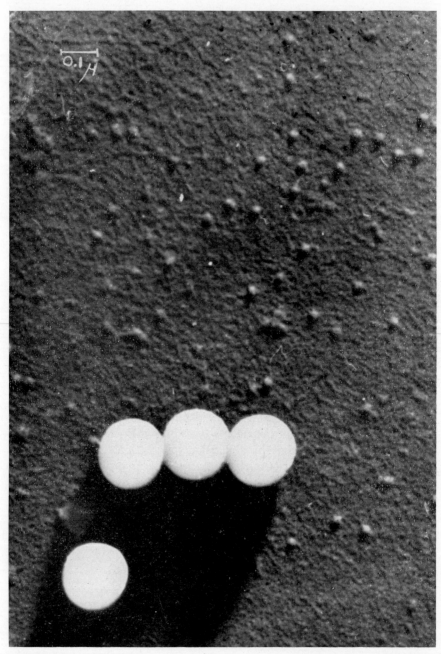

Fig. 5. Electron micrograph taken with a specimen of purified RNP. Shadow angle 3:1, RCA electron microscope. Polystyrene latex particles, 0.188-micron diameter, were used as internal standard.

REFERENCES

1. J. R. G. Bradfield, "Organization of bacterial cytoplasm," from *Bacterial Anatomy*, Cambridge University Press, 1956.

2. H. K. Schachman, A. B. Pardee, and R. Y. Stanier, *Arch. Biochem. Biophys., 38*, 245–260 (1952).

3. M. Alexander, *Bacteriol. Revs., 20*, 67–93 (1956).

4. S. Claesson, *Nature, 158*, 834 (1946).

5. Ace Glass Company, Vineland, New Jersey.

6. J. Wagman, E. Pollack, and E. J. Weneck, *Arch. Biochem. Biophys., 73*, 161–170 (1958).

7. M. L. Petermann and M. G. Hamilton, *J. Biophys. Biochem. Cytol., 1*, 469–472 (1955).

8. F.-C. Chao and H. K. Schachman, *Arch. Biochem. Biophys., 61*, 220 (1956).

9. M. R. McDonald, in *Methods in Enzymology* (Colowick and Kaplan, eds.), vol. 2, pp. 433–434, Academic Press, New York, 1955.

3

Stability of Ribonucleoprotein Particles
of *Escherichia coli*

ELLIS T. BOLTON

*Department of Terrestrial Magnetism
Carnegie Institution of Washington*

BILL H. HOYER   DANIEL B. RITTER

*Rocky Mountain Laboratory
National Institute of Allergy and Infectious Diseases
U. S. Public Health Service, Hamilton, Montana*

Investigations concerned with the structure and function of ribonucleoproteins of microorganisms require particle preparations that are representative, reproducible, and stable. This report presents some results of exploratory studies in which the analytical ultracentrifuge was used to assess the influence of various suspending media on the ribonucleoproteins of *Escherichia coli.*

METHODS

E. coli, B (ATCC 11303) harvested during the exponential phase of growth in a glucose-salts culture medium [1] was used for all studies. The bacteria were washed and resuspended (25 mg dry weight of bacteria per milliliter) in appropriate buffer solutions and disrupted by means of a modified French pres-

[1] The composition of C medium and other culture conditions may be found in Roberts et al., *Studies of Biosynthesis in Escherichia coli,* Carnegie Inst. Wash. Publ. 607, Washington, D. C., 1955.

18

sure cell[2] operated at approximately 10,000 psi. Breakage of the bacteria by this means is essentially complete. The resulting bacterial juices were examined in the analytical ultracentrifuge (Spinco, Model E) as soon as practicable (about 30 minutes after rupture), or after various periods of storage at 4° C. The centrifuge was routinely brought up to speed in 6 to 7 minutes and held at about 60,000 rpm for the duration of the run.

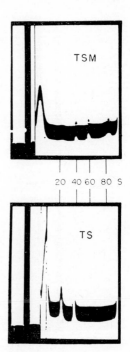

20 40 60 80 S

RESULTS

Figures 1 to 4 are illustrative sedimentation diagrams showing that the pattern of rapidly sedimenting components varies in accord with the kind of suspending medium used. Figure 1 compares the sedimentation behavior of the components in extracts prepared from bacteria broken in 0.01 M Tris–0.004 M succinic acid–0.005 M magnesium acetate buffer (pH 7.6, "TSM"), in 0.01 M Tris–0.004 M succinic acid ("TS"), or in TSM+0.07 M phosphate (pH 7.6). Values spotted along the abscissa are approximate apparent sedimentation coefficients. It is evident from this comparison that more, and larger, components are observed when magnesium has been included in the buffer and also that phosphate abolishes the more rapidly sedimenting materials. Whether the effect of phosphate is specific or whether the result is due to an increased ionic strength of the medium is not known. The sharp spike characteristic of highly polymerized deoxynucleic acid (DNA)[3] is missing from these diagrams, although it is readily observed in juices prepared by breaking *E. coli* as a result of lysozyme treatment and osmotic shock. In spite of this finding, three-quarters of the ultraviolet-absorbing substance and one-seventh of the protein of *E. coli* disrupted in the TSM medium may be sedimented in the preparative rotor (100,000g, 90 minutes).

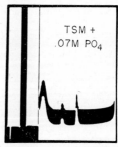

8 min 60,000 RPM

Fig. 1. Sedimentation diagrams of *E. coli* disrupted in various buffer solutions. The concentration of the bacterial juices differed among the runs.

Figure 2 shows that juices prepared by pressure cell disruption maintain constant sedimentation diagrams for at least 20 hours. If, however, sodium ethylenediaminetetraacetate (EDTA, 0.1 M, pH 7.6) is added to the bacterial extracts, all components greater than about 20 S disappear. This occurs whether

[2] C. S. French and H. W. Milner, *Methods in Enzymology I*, Academic Press, p. 65. A similar device is marketed by the American Instrument Company, Silver Spring, Maryland.

[3] See, for example, the sedimentation diagrams reported by W. Gillchriest and R. Bock, S. Dagley and J. Sykes, and J. Wagman reported in the present volume.

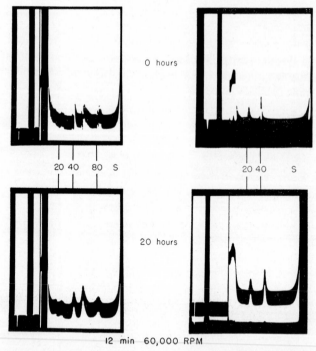

Fig. 2. Influence of storage at 4° C. The suspending buffers (TSM, left; TS, right) also contained 0.25 *M* sucrose, although subsequent runs have shown that sucrose has no effect on the pattern of components.

or not magnesium is included in the original suspending medium, as figure 3 demonstrates. In addition, a markedly decreased (<10 per cent) ultraviolet absorption occurs in the 100,000g–1 hour pellets (preparative rotor) when EDTA has been added to the bacterial juices. Figure 4 shows that DNAase (2 µg/ml) has little, if any, effect upon the number and size of the rapidly sedimenting materials, whereas RNAase (approximately 10 µg/ml) removes these components.

SUMMARY AND CONCLUSIONS

Pressure cell disruption of *E. coli* at *p*H 7.6 in magnesium-containing solutions of low ionic strength (e.g., 0.01 *M* Tris-succinate) releases high-molecular-weight components which range from 20 to 80 S. These components "fall apart," i.e., become elements having sedimentation coefficients less than about 20 S, when a chelater, EDTA, or the enzyme ribonuclease is allowed to act upon them. DNAase, sucrose, or cysteine exerts no apparent effect on either the number of components or their relative quantities. Nearly all (>80 per cent) of the ribonucleic acid and about one-seventh of the protein of *E. coli* can be sedimented in a preparative rotor under optimum conditions (TSM, 100,000g, 90 minutes). No RNA and only a trivial amount of protein can be sedimented after EDTA or ribonuclease treatment. Hence, it may be con-

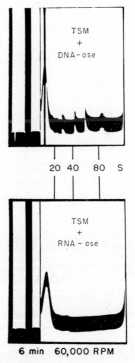

Fig. 3. Effect of EDTA on the sedimentation diagrams of *E. coli* juice. The two lower diagrams are from preparations containing one-half as much material as those for the upper pattern.

Fig. 4. Effect of nucleases on sedimentation diagrams. The lower pattern is from a, preparation one-half as concentrated as that of the upper diagram.

cluded that the bulk of the high-molecular-weight components of *E. coli* is composed of ribonucleoproteins held together in a fashion in which divalent cation(s) (probably Mg^{++}) and the integrity of ribonucleic acid play important roles. Thus, in certain physical and chemical attributes the "ribosomes" (ribonucleoprotein particles) of *E. coli* resemble constitutive elements of the cytoplasm of other bacteria, and also of yeast, plants, and mammals.

4

Biochemical Characterization and Electron-Microscopic Appearance of Microsome Fractions

DAVID GARFINKEL [1]

*Eldridge Reeves Johnson Foundation for Medical Physics
University of Pennsylvania*

The electron-microscope studies on microsomes by Palade and Siekevitz [1] have resulted in the definition of three kinds of microsomes: granules of 150 A diameter; smooth-surfaced vesicles; and rough-surfaced vesicles which differ in appearance from the smooth-surfaced ones primarily by having the granules attached to them. Biochemical studies of microsomes have resulted in the isolation of two varieties of microsomes—the 150 A granules just mentioned, which are the principal subject of interest in this symposium, and which are rich in RNA but poor in lipid and cytochrome b_5, and a particle isolated by Penn and Mackler [2] which is rich in cytochrome b_5 and lipid and poor in RNA. It will be shown here that there are at least three biochemically distinct varieties of microsomes, correlated with those observed in the electron microscope.

It is possible to fractionate mammalian liver microsomes (the work here described is with pig liver) so as to obtain, in addition to the microsomes as they are usually prepared, a small *light fraction* of microsomes which is usually found to contain about twice as much cytochrome b_5 and less than half as many ribonucleoprotein granules per unit biuret protein as the bulk of the microsomes, hereafter referred to as the *bulk fraction*. This fractionation may be made, for instance, by centrifuging a concentrated (1 part liver to 2 parts 0.25 M sucrose) homogenate, after the mitochondria have been removed, at

[1] Public Health Service Research Fellow of the National Cancer Institute, 1955–1957.

70,000g for 25 minutes. In addition to the bulk microsomal pellet, the light fraction is obtained as a suspension at the bottom of the centrifuge tube. In order to permit spectroscopic study, both fractions are washed with Ringer's solution, which removes the hemoglobin. It also washes out about 80 per cent of the RNA (although the ribonucleoprotein granules do not disintegrate and may still be isolated [3]), so that there are no accurate values for RNA concentration. It is found, however, that the bulk fraction contains appreciable non-cytochrome heme, somewhat more than the cytochrome heme, whereas the light fraction contains very little. A detailed description will be published elsewhere.

We have seen that the microsomes that centrifuge down last, the light fraction, are rich in cytochrome b_5. Palade and Siekevitz [1] found that they were likely to be smooth-surfaced. This finding suggests a correlation between smooth-surfaced appearance and the presence of cytochrome b_5. So does the fact that studies [4] in various tissues indicate that much of the cytochrome is present only where the electron microscope shows smooth-surfaced endoplasmic reticulum.

Drs. Ian R. Gibbons and T. F. Anderson kindly took photographs of one of these microsomal preparations with the electron microscope. Figure 1 shows views of the light and bulk fractions. It is seen that there is much more material of smooth-surfaced origin (free of the ribonucleoprotein granules) in the light fraction than in the bulk fraction. Counts of the numbers of smooth- and rough-surfaced microsomes, using unfixed preparations to avoid any enrichment of one microsomal type in the process of fixation, indicated that the percentage of smooth-surfaced microsomes was proportional to the cytochrome concentration (a light fraction which was twice as rich in cytochrome as the bulk fraction contained twice as many smooth-surfaced microsomes). Apparently cytochrome b_5 is localized in the smooth-surfaced microsomes and the rough-surfaced ones contain little of it. This observation is also in agreement with the fact that predominantly rough-surfaced microsomes can be prepared (from pancreas, for instance [4, 5]), and they contain little or no cytochrome. It would be desirable to confirm this by preparing pure smooth- or rough-surfaced microsomes and finding their cytochrome content (since the preparative method used enriches the smooth-surfaced microsomes only twofold, the resulting conclusions regarding their properties should not be considered final).

We are not limited to the electron microscope, but can also study the microsomes by biochemical methods. The procedure used here is digestion with pancreatin, a mixture of digestive enzymes from the pancreas. After digestion, which is not complete, what is left of the microsomes is centrifuged down and examined.

Initially, two suspensions of light and bulk microsomes have equal concentrations of cytochrome. Assuming that the smooth-surfaced microsomes contain nearly all the cytochrome, then their concentration is equal in the two suspensions. The protein concentrations are shown in table 1. The digestion

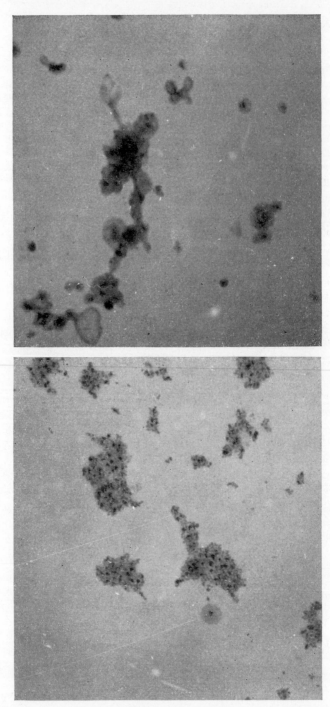

Fig. 1. Electron micrographs of light (above) and bulk (below) fraction microsomes, fixed with osmium tetroxide and air-dried from distilled water. Magnification 20,000×. The rough-surfaced microsomes may be identified by the little particles attached to them.

TABLE 1

| | Sedimentable Protein, mg/ml | |
	Light Fraction	Bulk Fraction
Before digestion	17	35
After digestion	8	20

for 10 days to 2 weeks is sufficient to solubilize nearly all the cytochrome; this is in fact the method of preparing cytochrome b_5 [6, 7]. The nucleoprotein granules have practically disappeared in the process. Examination of the sedimentable protein content of these two suspensions shows that much more protein is left in the bulk fraction. Nearly all the nucleoprotein has been removed, and since the cytochrome contents were equal there should be the same amount of residue from the smooth-surfaced microsomes in both fractions. Apparently there is something present in the bulk fraction (of which there is much less in the light fraction) to account for the difference in protein content. Since the other two forms were eliminated, this must be the rough-surfaced microsomes. That there is a qualitative difference in the residues can be seen by looking at the centrifuged pellets. Both contain a transparent amber layer, but this is all that is left of the light microsomes, whereas the bulk-fraction pellet has below this transparent layer an opaque tan one, showing some signs of further layering. This bulk-fraction pellet still contains the noncytochrome heme originally present. The rough-surfaced microsomes, which have not previously been characterized biochemically, are therefore found to contain a tan pigment and the noncytochrome heme, and to be distinct from the smooth-surfaced ones. This finding is summarized in table 2. It should be kept in mind that the expression "rough-surfaced microsomes" means the vesicles themselves

TABLE 2

| Particle | Cross-sectional Appearance in Electron Microscope | Isolated by | This Particle Is | |
			Rich in	Poor in
Ribonucleo-protein granule	Small, filled-in circle	Petermann and Hamilton [3]	RNA	Cytochrome b_5, noncytochrome heme
Smooth-surfaced microsome	Empty circle or ellipse	Penn and Mackler [2] (probably a fragment)	Cytochrome b_5, lipid	Noncytochrome heme (RNA?)
Rough-surfaced microsome	Empty circle or ellipse with small filled-in circles attached to outside		Lipid, noncytochrome heme, tan pigment	

without the attached granules. The fact that three varieties of microsomes have
been defined is not intended to imply that any of these varieties of microsomes
is itself homogeneous.

REFERENCES

1. G. E. Palade and P. Siekevitz, *J. Biophys. Biochem. Cytol., 2,* 171 (1956).

2. N. Penn and B. Mackler, *Federation Proc., 16,* 232 (1957).

3. M. L. Petermann and M. G. Hamilton, *J. Biol. Chem., 224,* 725 (1957).

4. D. Garfinkel, unpublished experiments.

5. G. E. Palade and P. Siekevitz, *J. Biophys. Biochem. Cytol., 2,* 671 (1956).

6. D. Garfinkel, *Arch. Biochem. Biophys., 70,* 111 (1957).

7. P. Strittmatter and S. F. Velick, *J. Biol. Chem., 221,* 253 (1956).

5

The Configurational Properties of Ribonucleic Acid Isolated from Microsomal Particles of Calf Liver

BENJAMIN D. HALL   PAUL DOTY

Department of Chemistry, Harvard University

Although ribonucleic acids (RNA) from many sources have been examined by physical methods within the last few years no clear and consistent picture of the configurational properties of RNA has materialized. Most studies of RNA have been complicated by spontaneous changes of molecular weight, aggregation under some conditions and degradation under others. In the work reported here we have avoided these complications by finding experimental conditions under which the RNA is stable and have then proceeded to establish its configurational properties in solution by means of several different physical methods.

The choice of microsomal particles from liver as our source of RNA was prompted by the particular importance that these ribonucleoprotein particles have assumed by virtue of their participation in protein synthesis [1, 2] and the fact that they can be isolated in pure form [3] before the preparation of the RNA itself.

It is important to emphasize at the outset that our major emphasis in the work reported here has been on the configurational properties of stable RNA isolated from these particles. We defer until a later time a report on the molecular weight and configuration of RNA within the microsomal particles and the relation of the work presented here to these properties.

THE PREPARATION OF RNA

Preparation of Microsomal Particles. The procedure summarized below evolved from those used by Zamecnik et al. [1] and by Petermann and Hamilton [4] for the isolation of similar particles from rat liver. Calf liver was

27

quickly frozen in Dry Ice within 3 minutes of slaughter, and thawed immediately before proceeding with the preparation. The liver was thoroughly chopped while thawing and the cell walls were broken by blending in an Osterizer Blendor intermittently for 3 to 4 minutes at about half speed. The suspending medium for this operation was ice-cold 0.25 M sucrose (2 cc/g liver).

The resulting suspension was centrifuged twice for 30 minutes at 1500g in the cold. The supernatant solution, containing the microsomes, glycogen, and soluble liver proteins, was removed by pipet after each centrifugation. The microsomal particles were then separated from the lipoprotein portion of the microsomes by emulsifying the microsomes with sodium deoxycholate [1]. A pellet of microsomal particles can then be obtained by ultracentrifugation of the deoxycholate-treated microsome suspension. To the supernate from the second low-speed centrifugation, 1/9 volume 5 per cent sodium deoxycholate (in 0.05 M Tris buffer, pH 8.2) was added with stirring. Stirring was continued for 15 minutes at 0° C. The microsomal particles were sedimented by centrifugation for 5 hours at 29,000 rpm in the no. 30 rotor of a Spinco model L ultracentrifuge. The dark red supernatant solution was removed from the microsomal-particle pellet by decantation. The pellet was used without further purification for preparing RNA. For studies on the microsomal particles, further centrifugation, both high- and low-speed, was employed to obtain microsomal particles free from contaminating proteins.

Properties of the Microsomal Particles. The degree of homogeneity of the particles is revealed by the sedimentation diagram shown in figure 1. Extrapolation of numerous measurements at various concentrations in the 0.025 M

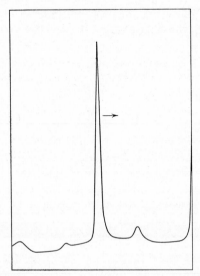

Fig. 1. Sedimentation diagram of microsomal particles in 0.025 M NaHCO$_3$, 0.004 M MgCl$_2$, pH 8.5. Picture taken at bar angle of 32° after 24 minutes at 27,690 rpm. $s_{20}=78.7$ at this concentration (1.2 g/dl); $s^0{}_{20}=81.3$.

NaHCO₃ containing 4 mM MgCl₂ (pH 8.5) yielded 81 for $s^0{}_{20,\,w}$. The ratio of optical densities at 260 and 280 mμ was 1.80 in this solvent. The ratio at 260 and 230 mμ was 1.32. Various mild treatments such as heating to 37° C cause the appearance of 50 S and 5 S components accompanied by increases in the optical density at 260 mμ (resembling the denaturation of DNA) and consequently increases in the values of the optical density ratios reported above.

Preparation of RNA from the Microsomal Particles. In order to obtain RNA of high purity from microsomal particles, two principal steps must of necessity be included in the procedure: (1) dissociation of the RNA from the protein; (2) separation of denatured proteins and other contaminating substances from the nucleic acid. This procedure makes use of one anionic detergent, sodium lauryl sulfate, to disrupt the protein–nucleic acid complex (by denaturing the protein and displacing the nucleic acid from cationic groups on the protein), and another, sodium xylene sulfonate (Naxonate), to remove the denatured protein from solution [5].

The pellet of microsomal particles was suspended in 0.01 M versene, pH 7.0. In a typical preparation, beginning with 200 g of liver, the volume of the suspension was 100 ml. The suspension was brought to 20° C, and sufficient solid sodium lauryl sulfate was added (with stirring) to bring the concentration to 4 per cent. Stirring was continued until a clear solution resulted; this was allowed to stand for 12 hours at 20° C. At the end of this time, the solution was cooled to 5° C, and to it were added 3 volumes of an ice-cold solution of 0.2 M KCl, 0.01 M versene pH 7.0 containing 12 g sodium xylene sulfonate per 100 cc. The pH of this mixture was reduced to 4.3 by dropwise addition of 6 N acetic acid. After standing 15 minutes at 0°, the suspension was centrifuged for 30 minutes at 1500g in the cold. The supernatant solution was decanted and brought to pH 7.0 by addition of 6 N NH₄OH. After the solution was warmed to 20° C, RNA was precipitated with 2 volumes isopropyl alcohol. The precipitate was allowed to settle for 2 hours; then it was centrifuged down. The liquid was decanted, and the RNA was dissolved in 0.03 M sodium acetate solution. This solution was treated with Naxonate to complete the removal of protein. To it were added 3 volumes 40 per cent Naxonate; then the solution was stirred for 30 minutes. After cooling to 0° C, the pH was brought to 4.3 and the solution was filtered through celite and sintered glass.[1] This treatment removed the protein-Naxonate complex, which is insoluble, leaving glycogen as the only nondialyzable impurity in the RNA. Glycogen may conveniently be removed by centrifugation for 20 minutes at 30,000g (it forms a pellet). After the removal of glycogen, the RNA solution was dialyzed against 0.01 M KH₂PO₄–K₂HPO₄ (1:1) in order to remove ultraviolet-absorbing impurities.

---

[1] It has recently been found that a substantial part of the RNA (up to 85 per cent of the total) is lost in this step because of adsorption on the celite. Besides lowering the yield, this may have led to fractionation of the RNA, if the adsorption was selective. This step may be omitted, for the protein-Naxonate aggregates can be removed along with glycogen in the centrifugation at 30,000g.

THE STABILIZATION OF RNA

The RNA prepared in the manner described above exhibited values of sedimentation constant and intrinsic viscosity that depended very much on the solvent employed, and invariably these quantities slowly diminished with time. Choosing 0.01 M phosphate buffer at pH 7.0 as solvent, typical preparations would have initially sedimentation constants of 9 and intrinsic viscosities of 0.6. The sedimentation pattern as observed in ultraviolet optics was rather broad and usually single peaked. The use of the above values in the Mandelkern-Flory equation [6] gave approximately 200,000 as the molecular weight.

In studying the gradual decay in molecular weight it was observed that heating to 60° C for a few minutes or the addition of KCNS to the extent of 0.2 M would cause a 30 per cent fall in molecular weight. This indicates that the polynucleotide chains of the original material were aggregated to a small but significant extent.

When the RNA was heated to progressively higher temperatures in the 0.01 M phosphate buffer the molecular weight was observed to continue falling up to temperatures of about 80° C. After exposure to 80° the molecular weight remained unchanged with time at room temperature, for prolonged periods at 83° and for short periods at 95°. Thus a single exposure to about 80° C produced a stabilization of the RNA.

The changes which such heating induced in the sedimentation pattern are shown in figure 2, where the sedimenting boundaries observed with ultraviolet optics under identical conditions are shown for 0, 5, 15, and 45 minutes' heating at 83° C. It is seen that the effect of the heating is to lower and to narrow the

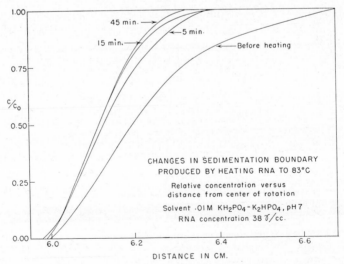

Fig. 2. Effect of heating upon RNA sedimentation boundaries after 21 minutes at 59,780 rpm.

sedimentation distribution; the change is nearly completed during the first 5 minutes of heating. The intrinsic viscosity showed a similar behavior. Both these changes indicate a fall in apparent molecular weight to a limiting value. The sharpening of the sedimentation distribution suggests a sharpening of the molecular-weight distribution as well. Consequently the fall in molecular weight appears to result from the dissociation of an aggregate and not the hydrolysis of phosphate ester bonds.

In order to proceed with the investigation of RNA stabilized by heating, a standard procedure was adopted: solutions in 0.01 M phosphate buffer were heated at 83° C for 10 minutes and then cooled to room temperature for measurement.

PROPERTIES OF RNA

The intrinsic viscosity and sedimentation constant measured for a number of preparations are listed in table 1. Recent results, shown in the lower part of the table, have consistently given sedimentation constants near 7 S, in contrast to variable and lower results obtained earlier, which are listed in the upper part of the table. RNA preparations having these higher and more consistent sedimentation values were obtained by improving the separation of the microsomal particles from other cellular fractions (thereby reducing ribonuclease contamination) and by maintaining a temperature of 5° or less at all stages of the preparation in which RNA might be attacked.

For a typical, improved preparation of stabilized RNA with $s^0_{25}=6.6$ S and the intrinsic viscosity $[\eta]=0.29$, a molecular weight (weight average) of 106,000 can be calculated from the Mandelkern-Flory equation [6] using 2.35×10^6 for $(\phi^{1/3}/P)$ and 0.55 for the partial specific volume. Light-scattering measurements on the same sample yielded the same value for the weight-average molecular weight.

TABLE 1.   Sedimentation Constant, Intrinsic Viscosity, and Molecular
Weight of RNA Preparations

Measured in 0.01 M phosphate, pH 7.0, after heating to 83° for 10 minutes.

s^0_{25}	$[\eta]_{25}$	$M_{s,[\eta]}$
2.9	0.14	21,700
4.1	0.17	40,700
4.6	0.19	50,400
5.0	. . .	. . . . .
6.2	0.26	93,000
6.6	0.29	106,000
6.6	. . .	. . . . .
7.1	. . .	. . . . .
7.4	0.27	120,000
6.8 ± 0.4	0.27	106,000

The agreement between the light-scattering molecular weight and that cal-culated from sedimentation and viscosity data justifies the application of the Mandelkern-Flory relation to the lower-molecular-weight samples listed in the upper part of table 1. The molecular-weight dependence of these two quan-tities can then be examined. This is done in figure 3, where the logarithms of s^0 and $[\eta]$ are plotted against the logarithm molecular weight, yielding the linear relations

$$s^0 = 2.1 \times 10^{-2} \; M^{0.49}$$
$$[\eta] = 6.2 \times 10^{-4} \; M^{0.53}$$

This type of dependence is associated with homologous samples of linear, ran-domly coiled polymer chains. These exponents are close to the limiting value of 0.5 which is reached for chains having the maximum permissible extent of coiling [7]. So high a degree of coiling is unexpected in a highly charged poly-electrolyte at the relatively low ionic strength used here and must be taken to indicate that the intrachain attractions are strong enough to overcome the ex-pansive electrostatic effect.

Provided that RNA is a randomly coiled, single chain, we should expect the relatively tight coiling to give way to a much more expanded coil in the ab-sence of added electrolyte. This would be recognized by a much higher viscosity and the further increase in the reduced specific viscosity upon dilution with water, a behavior known as the electroviscous effect in polyelectrolytes. When the RNA is transferred to aqueous solution (*p*H 5), its reduced specific viscosity at 0.6 g/dl is found to be 0.85 and to increase strikingly upon dilution. These results, shown in figure 4, clearly indicate the progressive expansion of the

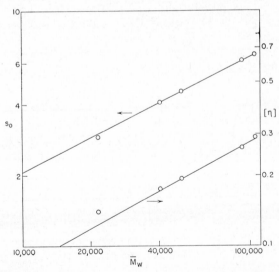

Fig. 3. Logarithmic dependence of the sedimentation constant and intrinsic viscosity of RNA upon the molecular weight.

molecule as its counterions become further removed from it. Upon the addition of salt the viscosity returns to a low value, showing the reversibility of the effect. Thus the solution properties of the RNA are found to be satisfactorily correlated with a randomly coiled, single-chain structure.

THE HYPOCHROMICITY OF RNA

In view of the substantial nucleotide attractions that appear to be necessary to account for the relatively tight coiling of RNA in 0.01 M phosphate buffer we sought to examine the possibility that hydrogen bonds between pairs of nucleotides were present in a random fashion within each coiled RNA molecule. Since the break-up of hydrogen bonds between base pairs in the denaturation of deoxyribose nucleic acid is accompanied by a substantial rise in ultraviolet absorbance [8], it seemed reasonable to look for the same effect in RNA. The hydrogen bonds that may exist in RNA would be broken during the expansion that was seen to accompany the removal of salt from the RNA solution. Alternatively such hydrogen bonds may be expected to be broken with increasing temperatures, as occurs with deoxyribose nucleic acid. We have combined these two hydrogen-bond-breaking effects by measuring the optical density of RNA solutions at 258 mμ as a function of temperature at various ionic strengths.

The results of this study are shown in figure 5. It is seen that in 0.01 M

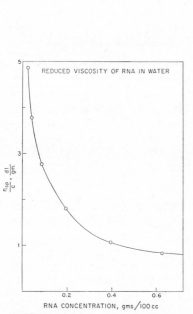

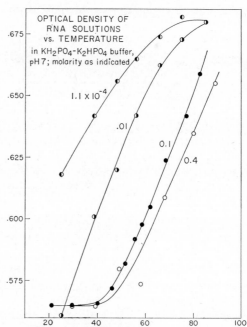

Fig. 4. Reduced specific viscosity of RNA in water; dependence on concentration.

Fig. 5. Variation of the optical density of RNA solutions at 258 mμ with temperature and ionic strength.

phosphate buffer the optical density rises at once as the temperature is raised above room temperature and reaches a maximum value, 28 per cent higher, at about 80° C. At higher ionic strength the rise is similar but does not begin until a higher temperature is reached. At lower ionic strength the optical density at room temperature is already considerably above the lower limiting value. Thus at the reduced ionic strength, where viscosity measurements show that the molecule is partly expanded, these measurements indicate that the hydrogen bonding is correspondingly reduced. These observations are consistent with the initial hypothesis and support the view that the intrachain attractions in RNA arise from hydrogen bonding between the purine and pyrimidine bases. The pairing would presumably be similar to that existing in DNA, but this fact carries no implication that the base pairs would be periodically organized.

Since the magnitude of the hypochromic effect (about 28 per cent) is more than half the total that results from the hydrolysis of RNA [9], the implication is that a large fraction of the purine and pyrimidines participate in the pairing when the ionic strength is 0.01 M or more. The fraction of base pairs involved appears to be unchanged by the heating cycle. Indeed, the first heating cycle of freshly prepared RNA shows the same results as successive cycles, in contrast with DNA, where the optical density never returns to the original value after the first heating. One would therefore conclude that there is no periodic arrangement of base pairs in RNA as there is in DNA.

Finally, it is of interest to note that the heat treatment used to stabilize the RNA, heating to 83° C of a 0.01 M phosphate buffer solution, is precisely the treatment required to reach the maximal optical density and presumably break the hydrogen bonds. Consequently the drop in apparent molecular weight produced by the heat treatment may have done nothing other than permit some aggregates of RNA molecules to be dissociated through the opening-up of the hydrogen bonds holding them together. It remains for future work to show whether or not this interchain bonding is a remnant of structural organization of RNA in the microsomal particle.

ACKNOWLEDGMENT

We are deeply indebted to Dr. Norman S. Simmons, Atomic Energy Project, University of California at Los Angeles, for his helpful advice and discussions regarding the preparation of RNA. One of us wishes to thank also the National Science Foundation and the Union Carbon and Carbide Corporation for fellowship support during the course of this investigation. This investigation was supported by the National Institutes of Health (C2170).

Note Added in Proof

Using aqueous phenol for removal of protein, we have isolated from calf-liver microsomal particles RNA of substantially higher molecular weight ($\sim 1 \times 10^6$) than that obtained in detergent RNA preparations. This large RNA appears to be composed of subunits which are single-chain coils of the type described here. When it is heated to 85° in 0.02 M phosphate buffer, the molecular weight falls to 120,000, the intrinsic viscosity to 0.22, and the sedimentation constant to 7.5.

REFERENCES

1. J. W. Littlefield, E. B. Keller, J. Gross, and P. C. Zamecnik, *J. Biol. Chem., 217,* 111 (1955).

2. P. C. Zamecnik, E. B. Keller, M. B. Hoagland, J. W. Littlefield, and R. B. Loftfield, *Ciba Foundation Symposium on Ionizing Radiations and Cell Metabolism,* pp. 161–168, Churchill, London, 1956.

3. M. L. Petermann, N. A. Mizen, and M. G. Hamilton, *Cancer Research, 16,* 620 (1956).

4. M. L. Petermann and M. G. Hamilton, *J. Biol. Chem., 224,* 725 (1957).

5. N. Simmons, private communication.

6. L. Mandelkern and P. J. Flory, *J. Chem. Phys., 20,* 212 (1952).

7. P. J. Flory, *Principles of Polymer Chemistry,* p. 622, Cornell University Press, Ithaca, N. Y., 1953.

8. R. Thomas, *Biochim. et Biophys. Acta, 14,* 231 (1954).

9. B. Magasanik in *The Nucleic Acids,* vol. 1, p. 393, Academic Press, New York, 1955.

6

Microsomes and Ribonucleoprotein Particles

GEORGE E. PALADE

The Laboratories of the Rockefeller Institute for Medical Research

I should like to present in the following pages a short history of the development of our present concepts on microsomes and ribonucleoprotein (RNP)
particles. I consider the historical background of this field of research interesting
in itself; moreover, I believe that its knowledge may throw some light on the
actual relations between microsomes and RNP particles as well as on some basic
principles of biological organization.

THE MICROSOMES

The discovery of the microsomes was a by-product of work done on virus-
induced tumors by Albert Claude at the Rockefeller Institute in the late 1930's.
Trying to purify a tumor-inducing fraction obtained by differential centrifugation from breis of Rous sarcomata,[1] Claude found as expected that the preparation was rich in ribonucleic acid (RNA) [1], and was inactivated by various
agents known to affect nucleoproteins and nucleic acids [2]. At the same time,
however, he unexpectedly discovered that cell fractions, similar in their gross
chemistry to the tumor-inducing preparations, could be isolated from chick
embryos [3], and from a variety of tissues, adult as well as embryonic, and
normal as well as tumorous [4, 5]. From the beginning Claude was convinced
that these fractions consisted of pre-existing cell structures, not of cytoplasmic
aggregates artificially produced by tissue grinding. After some hesitation,[2] he
[4, 5] arrived at the conclusion that the structures involved were new cell
components of widespread occurrence which had eluded detection by light
microscopy because they were too close to, or below, the limit of resolution of

---

[1] Chicken tumor I.

[2] For a while he assumed that the fraction consisted of mitochondria or mitochondrial
fragments.

usual light optics.[3] In his early reports he described the new components as "small particles" or "small granules"; later he chose the term "microsomes" (small bodies) [6, 7], which met with favor and has remained in common use ever since. From his centrifugation data,[4] Claude calculated that the microsomes measured ~ 50 to 200 mμ in diameter, and on the strength of his chemical analyses he defined them as "phospholipide-ribonucleoprotein complexes" [4, 5]. In this way and thus defined the microsomes entered the biochemical thinking of our times.

Claude's discovery was followed by an extensive period of biochemical research which confirmed and greatly extended his findings. For practical reasons, the research effort was concentrated almost exclusively on liver, and as a result the voluminous literature thereby produced (for reviews see [8, 9, 10]) applies primarily to liver microsomes, not, as usually assumed, to microsomes in general. According to this literature, the dominant biochemical feature of the microsomal fraction is its high RNA content: ~ 40 to 50 per cent of the RNA of the tissue brei is usually recovered in the microsomes, together with ~ 15 per cent of its proteins. Consequently the microsomal RNA/protein ratio is high— until recently higher than that of any other cell fraction. It should be mentioned, however, that, with all this concentration, the RNA does not represent more than ~ 10 per cent of the microsomal dry weight. Another apparently characteristic feature of the fraction is its large content and high concentration of phospholipides: ~ 50 per cent of the phospholipides of the tissue are recovered in the microsomes. As far as biochemical activities are concerned, the microsomes are distinguished by high concentrations of diphosphopyridine nucleotide–cytochrome c reductase [11], cytochrome m or b_5 [12, 13], and glucose-6-phosphatase [14], and especially by their ability to incorporate labeled amino acids into their proteins both *in vivo* [15–19] and *in vitro* [20–22]. According to current interpretations, the last property indicates that the microsomes are, or contain, the sites of protein synthesis of the cytoplasm.

In contrast with the active and diversified work on the biochemical aspects of the problem, research on the identity of the microsomes, or of their precursors, inside the intact cell made little progress because of a number of technical limitations. Of the instruments available for morphological investigation,

---

[3] The microsomes can be seen as distinct particles in the dark-field microscope [5], and as a shimmering mass of indistinct small bodies in the light microscope, especially under phase contrast optics.

[4] For Claude the microsomes were the fraction sedimented in 1 hour at 18,000g from the supernatant of the "large granule" (mitochondrial) fraction. The medium he used in preparing tissue "extracts" was either water or dilute phosphate buffer or 0.15 M NaCl. When sucrose solutions were introduced in cell-fractionation procedures, the centrifugal force was increased to compensate for the higher density and viscosity of the new medium. At present the microsomes are usually separated by centrifuging a mitochondrial supernatant for 1 hour at $\sim 100,000g$, irrespective of the sucrose concentration in the suspending medium. Since this concentration varies from 0.25 to 0.88 M, the microsome fractions described in the literature are not strictly comparable to one another.

one—the light microscope—did not have enough resolving power, and the other —the electron microscope, introduced in biological research at the time of the discovery of the microsomes—could provide the necessary resolution but preparatory techniques for the electron microscopy of biological specimens were still inadequate. As a result the microsomes remained until recently a cytochemical concept only, without a known structural counterpart in the organization of the intact cell. Many cytologists and cytochemists even doubted that these small bodies were derived from a pre-existing cell structure and were inclined to consider them artifacts due to cytoplasmic clumping or mitochondrial fragmentation [23] during the homogenization of the tissue.

Because of their characteristically high content of RNA, the microsomes were rather early correlated with the so-called "basophil substance" of the cytoplasm. Although the correlation was based on circumstantial evidence obtained on a limited number of cell types [7, 24], it was soon assumed to be generally valid, and consequently the microsomes and the basophil cytoplasm began to be regarded as equivalent terms in two different technical vocabularies. An apparent convergence was thus effected between two lines of cytochemical research: an old line exemplified by the work of Brachet's (cf. [25]) and Cassperson's (cf. [26]) groups and aiming at the localization of nucleic acids *in situ,* and a new line based on cell-fractionation procedures. The correlation appeared to be further strengthened when the large body of circumstantial evidence accumulated by Brachet and Cassperson on the role of RNA in protein synthesis received full and repeated support from experiments showing that the microsomes were the most active cell fraction in the incorporation of labeled amino acids into proteins.

The lack of morphological information, the concentration of the work on liver, and the equation of the microsomes with the basophil substance of the cytoplasm had some unfavorable consequences on the development of general ideas in the field. It was assumed, for instance, without enough evidence, that entities similar or identical to Claude's microsomes existed in all cells, bacterial cells included, and it was also believed that the chemical composition of liver microsomes was representative for microsomes in general. As we shall see, both assumptions are now in need of revision.

THE ENDOPLASMIC RETICULUM

I shall turn now to another development, in a different field, which from the beginning seemed to have some connection with our main problem. A few years after the discovery of the microsomes, and again in conjunction with work done on Rous sarcomata, Porter, Claude, and Fullam [27] and Claude, Porter, and Pickels [28] succeeded in obtaining electron micrographs of thinly spread cells (avian fibroblasts) maintained in tissue culture. Below the limit of resolution of the light microscope and well within the range of calculated microsomal sizes, they found a "lace-like" network of slightly higher density than the rest of the cytoplasm. Porter, continuing the study of this structure in cultured material, arrived at the conclusion that it consisted of vesicles and tubules interconnected in a continuous network. Since the network was restricted to the inner or endoplasmic region of the cytoplasm, he proposed the name endoplasmic reticulum for the entire structure [29, 30]. The discovery of this network provided a likely candidate for the role of microsomal precursor within the intact cell, and indeed both Claude [31] and Porter [30] speculated that the microsomes might represent derivatives of the endoplasmic reticulum, but the assumption could not be verified at the time because the electron microscopy of cells and tissues was still in infancy. The examination of a liver cell, for instance, was a difficult and uncertain project; in fact, the first attempt [32] to identity "microsomes" in electron micrographs of sectioned hepatic cells yielded misleading results.[5]

In the early 1950's, however, a succession of technical improvements covering the whole series of preparative steps [33, 34] but affecting primarily microtomy [35, 36] made possible the examination of thin sections of practically all cell types in the electron microscope. With this spectacular breaking through the barriers of technical difficulties, the search for the intracellular equivalents of the microsomes finally became possible. But most electron microscopists engaged at that time in the study of the fine structure of the cell were not directly interested in the microsome problem; they were rather attracted by a related question: namely that of the structural substrate of cytoplasmic basophilia. Apparently it did not matter, because, as already mentioned, the two problems were expected to have a common solution. In the newly opened realm of fine cellular organization the microscopists found an unsuspected and, at the beginning, puzzling abundance of structures. After a few years spent in deciphering these findings and in arguing about various interpretations,[6] it became clear that the ground substance of the cytoplasm contained an extensive system of spaces, described as vesicles, tubules, and cisternae [7] (figs. 1 and 2), limited by a thin membrane (~ 7 mμ) and interconnected in a more or less continuous network.

It was soon realized that the so-called ground substance of the cytoplasm was divided into two distinct phases by the existence of this internal membrane system: one represented by the content of the interconnected vesicles, the other by the surrounding cytoplasmic matrix. It was also observed that small, dense particles, ~ 15 mμ in diameter, appeared to be attached to the membrane (on the surface facing the cytoplasmic matrix) in certain parts of the reticulum (fig. 2) while other parts remained free. In addition, it was found that similar particles occurred apparently freely scattered throughout the cytoplasmic matrix

[5] Masses of glycogen were apparently taken for microsomes.

[6] Representative samples of the various interpretations advanced can be found in references 37 to 39.

[7] The term designates flat, shallow vesicles which measure only 50 to 70 mμ in depth but reach into microns in the other two directions.

(fig. 2). Work done in our laboratory established that the system corresponds to the endoplasmic reticulum of cultured cells [40], and subsequent observations showed that a number of local differentiations occur within this continuous network which appears to possess, for instance, a rough-surfaced part [40, 41], on account of the attached particles already described, and a smooth-surfaced [40, 41] or agranular [42] part free of such particles. Frequently the elements of the system, particularly its cisternae, show preferred orientation and seem to be disposed parallel to one another at more or less regular intervals, thus forming stacks or piles of various sizes (figs. 1 and 2). Finally, further work showed that the system varies characteristically from one cell type to another and that these variations affect the total volume of the system, the relative extent of its rough- and smooth-surfaced parts, as well as the extent of preferential orientation encountered within the system [38].

The Structural Substrate of Cytoplasmic Basophilia. With the limited information initially available, it was believed that the endoplasmic reticulum as a whole was the structural substrate of basophilia, but subsequent observations brought forward serious discrepancies between the distribution of the reticulum on one side and that of basophilia on the other. It was found, for instance, that there are cell types with an intensely basophil cytoplasm in which the endoplasmic reticulum is poorly developed. Such cells, however, have a large population of small, dense particles, most of them freely scattered in the cytoplasm [43]. The erythroblasts and the undifferentiated cells of rapidly growing epithelia (epithelia of the intestinal crypts, stratum germinativum of the epidermis) belong to this category. A converse situation is encountered in mature leucocytes and in seminal epithelia (rat) whose acidophil cytoplasm contains a relatively well developed endoplasmic reticulum, most of it smooth-surfaced, but has only a few small particles, free or attached.

In all the cases examined, the cytoplasmic component whose distribution matched best that of the affinity for basic dyes appeared to be represented by the small, dense particles. As a result of these findings, in 1953 I advanced [44, 43] the hypothesis that these particles, rather than the membranous material of the endoplasmic reticulum, contained most of the RNA of the cytoplasm, and that they were consequently the sought-for structural substrate of cytoplasmic basophilia. The hypothesis rested upon the results of a broad survey of various cell types which covered a large number of "test specimens," i.e., cells known for the intensity and characteristic distribution of "basophil substance" in their cytoplasm, as well as cells known for their cytoplasmic acidophilia. The postulate derived additional support from the fact that at that time small particles in the same size range and containing a large amount of RNA had already been isolated from yeast and bacterial cells [45] by Schachman et al., and from certain mammalian tissues, such as liver and spleen, by Petermann et. al. [46, 47].

From the beginning the hypothesis implied that the small particles and the endoplasmic reticulum represent two basically distinct components of the cytoplasm which may exist and develop independently of each other. Their close and more or less extensive association was considered a secondary phenomenon that occurs at a relatively late stage in the evolution of cellular organization. The view, originally based on findings on undifferentiated or embryonic cells, subsequently received full support from electron-microscope studies of various bacteria [48, 49, 50] which revealed that bacterial protoplasm contains a large population of small, dense particles (usually smaller than those found in animal cytoplasm), but apparently no internal membranous system comparable to the endoplasmic reticulum [50].

A Correlated Morphological and Biochemical Analysis of Hepatic Microsomes. The next task was to put the hypothesis to a test by trying to find out in what cell fractions the particles segregate during the differential centrifugation of tissue breis. Fraction chemistry and particle distribution were correlated by using duplicate pellets of the fractions under study: one pellet for biochemical analysis, and the other for electron microscopy after appropriate fixation, embedding, and sectioning. It was found both necessary and expeditious to fix the pellets *in toto,* and to cut them in such a way as to be able to survey them from top to bottom. With such precautions, the existence and the extent of inter-contamination among cell fractions could be easily detected and the presence of distinct layers in some pellets clearly demonstrated.

The work, carried out in collaboration with Dr. Philip Siekevitz, started with an analysis of the microsomal fraction isolated from rat-liver breis [51]. We found that this fraction consists almost exclusively of closed vesicles limited by a dense continuous membrane, ~ 7 mμ thick, and filled with a material of relatively low density. Most of these vesicles are derived from the rough-surfaced part of the endoplasmic reticulum as indicated by the small (~ 15 mμ), dense particles attached to the outer surface of their limiting membrane. Smooth-surfaced vesicles are also present in the microsomal fraction, but their origin is more difficult to ascertain; they may represent fragments of the smooth-surfaced part of the reticulum or they may be derived from other sources (Golgi complex?[8] cell membrane?). In 0.88 M sucrose, the medium used in our experiments, the microsomal vesicles retained the flattened appearance of intracellular cisternae and reacted like osmometers to changes in the concentration of the medium: they swelled in hypotonic media. Treatment with versene (2 per cent in 0.88 M sucrose, for 60 minutes at $0°$ C) removed ~ 60 per cent of the microsomal RNA and resulted in extensive loss of attached particles. Incubation in ribonuclease (0.5 mg/ml 0.88 M sucrose; 60 minutes at $37°$ C) caused RNA losses of ~ 85 per cent and produced a heavy agglutination of microsomal vesicles. During the incubation, the attached particles apparently were lost. Finally treatment with sodium deoxycholate (DOC) (0.5 per cent in 0.88 M sucrose, at pH 7.5) "solubilized" most of the protein and phospholipides of the

---

[8] According to our interpretation [38], the "Golgi complex" is a differentiated part of the endoplasmic reticulum. Other cytologists [52] consider this structure a distinct and independent cell organelle.

microsomes, but left ∼ 80 per cent of their RNA and ∼ 15 per cent of their protein still in sedimentable form. The pellets obtained from DOC-treated microsomes consisted of small, dense particles ∼ 10 to 15 mμ in diameter with a small admixture of vesicles. We interpreted the results as indicating that DOC "solubilizes" the membrane and content of the microsomal vesicles while affecting their attached particles to a lesser extent, and we inferred from these experiments that the small, dense particles consist of ribonucleoprotein and contain most of the microsomal RNA (∼ 80 per cent), while the membrane and content account for most of the protein and almost all the phospholipides of the microsomes [51].

We soon found out that, contrary to assumptions then current, the final supernatant still contained numerous structured elements of membranous or particulate nature, and accordingly we made an attempt to separate these elements by further centrifugation of the microsomal supernatant, the fraction usually considered the liquid phase of the cytoplasm or the "cell sap." We isolated two successive postmicrosomal fractions [9] in the hope that one of them might consist mainly of free particles, but we found the corresponding pellets to be mixtures of smooth-surfaced vesicles (probably derived from the smooth-surfaced part of the reticulum), free particles, and amorphous material. The RNA content of these postmicrosomal fractions was low, and its concentration therein considerably lower than in the microsomes [51].

In the case of the liver we succeeded, therefore, in identifying the microsomes as fragments of the endoplasmic reticulum, derived primarily from its rough-surfaced part. We obtained evidence indicating that they are closed vesicles, and that most of their RNA is present as ribonucleoprotein in their attached particles. We did not succeed in isolating the free particles of the cytoplasmic matrix, nor did we obtain a "clean" preparation of smooth-surfaced vesicles. The information on the gross chemistry of microsomal membranes was indirect and relied on subtractions and many assumptions.

PANCREATIC MICROSOMAL AND POSTMICROSOMAL FRACTIONS

As the next object for testing our hypothesis, we chose the pancreas of the guinea pig with the following considerations in mind. The exocrine cells, which form the bulk of the cell population of the gland, have an endoplasmic reticulum remarkable in its large volume and in the small extent of its smooth-surfaced part (figs. 1 and 2). In addition, their cytoplasmic matrix contains free particles in great numbers (fig. 2). With the new material, therefore, we stood a better chance to obtain a more homogeneous microsomal fraction and to separate free particles in a postmicrosomal fraction. The results met our expecta-

---

[9] The first postmicrosomal fraction (PM_1) was obtained by centrifuging the microsomal supernatant for 2 hours at 105,000g; the second postmicrosomal fraction (PM_2), by centrifuging the supernatant of PM_1 for 16 hours at 105,000 g.

tions. We found that pancreatic microsomes [53] are closed vesicles (figs. 4 and 5) almost exclusively derived from the rough-surfaced part of the cells' voluminous reticula. They are, however, more labile structures than their hepatic counterparts: even when isolated in 0.88 M sucrose they enspherulate and do not retain the flattened cisternal form that the elements of the endoplasmic reticulum have *in situ*. They are also more susceptible to various treatments, especially to deoxycholate, which, at 0.3 per cent final concentration, solubilizes $\sim$ 85 per cent of their protein and $\sim$ 40 per cent of their RNA. As in the case of the liver, the DOC-insoluble material consists of RNA particles (fig. 6) with a relatively high RNA/protein ratio. The main difference between hepatic and pancreatic microsomes concerns their phospholipide content: there is $\sim$ 8 times less phospholipide in pancreatic microsomes than in their hepatic counterparts, and the phospholipide concentration in the microsomal fraction is equal to, or only slightly higher than, that in the original pancreatic brei.

Centrifugation of the microsomal supernatant resulted in the sedimentation of further material which was arbitrarily divided into two postmicrosomal fractions [9] (PM_1 and PM_2). We found that the corresponding pellets consist almost exclusively of small, dense particles $\sim$ 15 mμ in diameter (fig. 7), with a moderate admixture of small vesicles in the PM_1. Chemically both fractions were made up of ribonucleoproteins with a negligible amount of phospholipides. In the original fractionation scheme [53], the two postmicrosomal fractions contained RNA in comparable concentrations, but in a recent modification PM_1 has a noticeably higher RNA/protein ratio than PM_2.

The results obtained with the pancreas confirmed and extended our previous findings on liver. In both the microsomes were found to be vesicles derived either to a large extent [51], or almost exclusively [53], from the rough-surfaced part of the endoplasmic reticulum. We used a characteristic structural detail, namely the attached particles, to establish this derivation, and our conclusion appears reasonably valid; there is good general agreement between the basic morphological features of the microsomes and the fine structural details of the endoplasmic reticulum. There is, however, no agreement as far as general dimensions are concerned: the network is a continuous structure which may spread throughout the entire cytoplasm of the intact cell ($\sim$ 20$\times$ $\sim$ 30$\times$ $\sim$ 40 μ), whereas the microsomes are considerably smaller (0.05 to 0.3 μ), corresponding in dimensions to the vesicles, tubules, and cisternae which by their interconnections form the reticulum. Accordingly we must assume that the network is broken during tissue grinding, the resulting fragments being the microsomes. Since these fragments are closed vesicles, we are further obliged to postulate that the broken segments heal readily into closed structures or that the fragmentation of the reticulum occurs by a generalized pinching-off process rather than by mechanical disruption [51, 53].

DIVERSITY OF CYTOPLASMIC RIBONUCLEOPROTEINS

The view that the small, dense particles represent the structural substrate of cytoplasmic basophilia was clearly supported by the isolation of RNP particles from DOC-treated microsomes (fig. 6) and further strengthened by the finding that the pancreatic postmicrosomal fractions (fig. 7), assumed to represent the free particles of the cytoplasmic matrix, are also comprised of ribonucleoproteins. It should be pointed out, however, that the RNP particles, free and attached, do not account for all the RNA of the cytoplasm. Leaving aside the controverted question of the RNA content of mitochondria, we found that the microsomes contain a certain amount of RNA, small in the liver but relatively large in the pancreas, which is solubilized by DOC treatment, under the conditions of our experiments, and whose structural connections are unknown. Finally there is a relatively small amount of RNA ($\sim$ 10 per cent of the RNA of the cytoplasm) that remains in the supernatant of the last postmicrosomal fraction. Evidently we do not know to what extent our findings reflect the situation inside the living cell, or to what extent they are affected by preparation artifacts. It can be argued, for instance, that attached particles can be detached during tissue grinding and fractionation, or that the sedimentation of RNA particles is still incomplete by the end of our last centrifugation.

With such possibilities in mind, Dr. Siekevitz and I tried to find out in more recent work [54] whether there are functional differences among the various RNP preparations described. In agreement with reports on other tissues [55, 56], we noted that the attached particles (DOC-insoluble microsomal material) are more active than the parental microsomes in the incorporation of labeled amino acids into proteins (presumably protein synthesis[10]). In addition, we found that the activity mentioned is considerably higher in the attached particles than in the free RNP particles of the postmicrosomal fractions. The second postmicrosomal fraction, however, proved to be more active than any other particulate fraction in the incorporation of labeled adenine into RNA. In turn, its activity was greatly exceeded by that of the "soluble" RNA of the final supernatant.

Such metabolic differences, though not entirely excluding preparation artifacts, render them more unlikely, and suggest that a variety of RNP's with different structural connections and different functions exist within the animal cell. I should also add that by comparing microsomes obtained from starved and fed animals we observed a relatively large increase in microsomal proteolytic[11] and ribonuclease activity [57]. What seems to be of considerable interest is the finding that a sizable part of the enzymatic activities of the micro-

---

[10] In our experiments the incorporation was carried out *in vivo;* in those reported in references 55 and 56 the labeled amino acids were incorporated either *in vivo* or *in vitro* by whole microsomes.

[11] Due mainly to trypsinogen and chymotrypsinogen. These two proteases and the ribonuclease are enzymes synthesized on a large scale by the exocrine cells of the pancreas to be released in the intestine for the digestion of food.

somes is found associated with their attached RNP particles. Further work will show whether these enzymes are newly synthesized proteins still attached to their sites of synthesis or enzymes released from other locations and absorbed on RNP particles during tissue grinding.

DIFFERENCES BETWEEN MICROSOMES AND RNP PARTICLES

It follows from the results thus far summarized that the cytoplasm contains more separable entities than were assumed a few years ago. It also follows that Claude's microsomes are relatively large and complex structures in which membranous and particulate components can be easily recognized. There is also a microsomal content which, though usually amorphous, may occur as formed granules ([57], cf. [58]) under certain conditions, thus increasing the complexity of the structure. The term "microsomal particles," used in many communications made at this meeting, can be properly applied to RNP particles attached to the surface of microsomal vesicles. As already indicated, such particles can be detached by DOC treatment and subsequently collected in relatively clean preparations. It is doubtful, however, that the same term can be used to designate the free RNP particles isolated in postmicrosomal fractions and especially RNP particles separated from bacterial cells, in which there is no endoplasmic reticulum to start with, and from which no microsomes can be obtained. Pellets obtained from bacteria are composed of much smaller and simpler cell components which morphologically seem to correspond to the free RNP particles of the pancreatic cell. In general, a morphological label is justified as long as there is no information on the chemistry and function of the structure involved. Here, however, we know that we are dealing with ribonucleoprotein particles, and consequently there is not too much sense in retaining a morphological label, especially after realizing that it is misleading.

More than accurate terminology is involved in this argument. What is known so far about the fine structure of bacterial cells suggests that internal membranous systems, like the endoplasmic reticulum, are not necessary for the organization and function of a simple type of self-sustaining cell. Such membranous systems appear in more elaborate cell forms and could therefore be regarded as superstructures. We do not know what special problems are solved by their introduction, but we may wonder whether they are not connected with an increase in cell volume, subsequent difficulties in diffusion, and relative decrease in available surface. At higher levels of biological organization, similar problems are frequently encountered and usually solved by the invagination of surface structures and by the concomitant interiorization of part of the surrounding medium. There is therefore an important difference in organization between bacterial cells on one side, and animal and plant cells on the other: the superstructure that can be ground into microsomes appears only in the latter. Terms such as "microsomes" or "microsomal particles" of bacterial origin do not take this basic difference into account.

RECENT INFORMATION ON CYTOPLASMIC BASOPHILIA AND RNP PARTICLES

During the past 5 years considerable progress has been made in the study of cell organization through the extensive use of electron microscopy and cell-fractionation procedures. Accordingly it is of interest to see how the hypothesis formulated in 1953 has fared through this period of rapid development.

The assumption that the small particulate component of the cytoplasm is the structural substrate of basophilia has remained in good agreement with the large majority of the findings made on new and very numerous cell types of animal and plant origin (see for examples [59, 60]). The only exception so far encountered is represented by the heart muscle of the turtle [61], in which a slightly larger particulate was found in an acidophil cytoplasm that gave a positive test for glycogen. Consequently it was postulated that particulate glyco-gen might be mistaken for RNP particles in certain cell types, especially in muscle [61]. The actual isolation of this particulate material from various muscle fibers could settle the question, but so far it has not been accomplished. It should be pointed out, however, that under prevailing technical conditions a certain amount of confusion of the type suggested cannot be excluded. Because of the dimensions involved, we are examining only the gross morphology of the small particles, and in so doing we are not helped thus far by any charac-teristic detail of structure. If particles of different chemical composition and of different fractions happen to have the same general size and shape, we cannot avoid lumping them together in a common category. Morphological expressions that can be distinguished at the present level of practical resolution are un-doubtedly less numerous than functional characteristics or macromolecular species. It is exactly for this reason that morphological information should be supplemented, wherever possible, by biochemical and metabolic data.

Ribonucleoprotein particles, with a sedimentation constant of 70 to 80 S and a calculated or measured diameter of 10 to 15 mμ, have been isolated from many new and old sources such as liver [62, 65], yeast [63], ascites cells [56], and pea seedlings [64]. They have been described in terms of their gross chemistry [62–65], biochemical activities [56], and physicochemical properties [62–65]. A perusal of this symposium shows that recently RNP particles have also been isolated from a variety of bacterial cells. In general, there is good agreement between these findings and our observations, but there is little or no information about the existence, frequency, and topography of the particles *in situ.*

Finally it is still debated whether the microsomal RNA is mainly located in the attached particles or is also present in large amounts in the microsomal membranes as originally assumed by Kuff et al. [66]. As already mentioned, an exclusive RNA location in the attached particles cannot be claimed because the particles do not account for ~ 20 per cent of the microsomal RNA in the liver and for ~40 per cent in the pancreas. Recently Chauveau et al. [67] found that there is no good correlation between the frequency of vesicles with attached particles and the amount of RNA present in microsomal pellets. They indicate, however, that particles appear after treating predominantly membranous pellets with DOC, and they suggest that the particles could be masked by incorporation into the membrane under certain uncontrolled conditions. It is evident that we should know more about the behavior of these particles under various metabolic conditions, and about their reaction to various suspension media used in tissue fractionation, before arriving at an understanding of these conflicting pieces of evidence.

CONCLUSIONS AND COMMENTS

In conclusion it can be said that small ($\sim$ 15 mμ), dense particles have been found, either free or attached to the membrane of the endoplasmic reticulum, in practically all animal and plant cells thus far examined. Comparable particles, usually unattached to membranous structures, exist in bacterial cells. The distribution of these particles is largely similar to that of cytoplasmic basophilia, by implication to that of cytoplasmic RNA.

Ribonucleoprotein particles of relatively small size (10 to 20 mμ and 40 to 80 S) have been isolated by various procedures, such as ultracentrifugation and electrophoresis, from a variety of animal, plant, and bacterial sources. Evidence that the small, dense particles seen in the intact cell consist of ribonucleoprotein has been obtained for the liver (rat) and the pancreas (guinea pig). Accordingly the assumption that these particles are the structural substrate of basophilia has been verified for two cell types only. For all the others, it remains what it has been, a hypothesis to be tested by further work. Integrated studies providing an adequate coverage from cell to pellets are evidently needed for more kinds of tissues.

Although it appears that the RNP particles are cytoplasmic components of widespread occurrence, probably basic structural elements in the organization of the cell, many points in their history are still uncertain or controverted, and many pertinent questions remain unanswered. For instance, though there is good agreement about the presence of RNA in particles, there is still doubt about the presence or absence of RNA in membranous structures, primarily in the membrane of the endoplasmic reticulum. Considerable variation occurs, apparently connected with the methods of preparation, in the RNA content of these particles; accordingly one would like to know the procedure by which the situation *in situ* is more closely approximated. There is morphological, physicochemical, and metabolic diversity among these particles, but very little is known about the way in which the various differences are correlated, or about the significance of this diversity. In this respect one may wonder whether particles with different locations and activities represent distinct, fully developed cell organs, or whether they correspond to successive stages in the differentiation of a single or a few cell organs. What seems to be particularly disturbing at present is the meagerness of our information about the functional role of these particles. Without more knowledge on this aspect, progress is uncertain even if it takes the appearance of elegant physicochemical data.

REFERENCES

1. A. Claude, *J. Exptl. Med., 66,* 59 (1937).

2. A. Claude and A. Rothen, *J. Exptl. Med., 71,* 619 (1940).

3. A. Claude, *Proc. Soc. Exptl. Biol. Med., 39,* 398 (1938).

4. A. Claude, *Science, 91,* 77 (1940).

5. A. Claude, *Cold Spring Harbor Symposia Quant. Biol., 9,* 263 (1941).

6. A. Claude, *Science, 97,* 451 (1943).

7. A. Claude, Frontiers in cytochemistry, in *Biol. Symposia, 10,* Jaques Cattell Press, Lancaster, Pa., 1943.

8. C. de Duve and J. Berthet, *Intern. Rev. Cytol., 3,* 225 (1954).

9. G. H. Hogeboom and W. C. Schneider, The cytoplasm, in *The Nucleic Acids, 2* (E. Chargaff and J. N. Davidson, editors), Academic Press, New York, 1955.

10. G. H. Hogeboom, E. L. Kuff, and W. C. Schneider, *Intern. Rev. Cytol., 6,* 425 (1957).

11. G. H. Hogeboom, *J. Biol. Chem., 177,* 847 (1949).

12. C. F. Strittmatter and E. G. Ball, *J. Cellular Comp. Physiol., 43,* 57 (1954).

13. M. Bailie and R. K. Morton, *Nature, 176,* 111 (1955).

14. H. G. Hers, J. Berthet, L. Berthet, and C. de Duve, *Bull. soc. chim. biol., 33,* 21 (1951).

15. H. Borsook, C. L. Deasy, A. J. Haagen Smit, G. Keighley, and P. H. Lowry, *J. Biol. Chem., 196,* 669 (1952).

16. T. Hultin, *Exptl. Cell Research, 1, 376,* 599 (1950).

17. N. D. Lee, J. T. Anderson, R. Miller, and R. H. Williams, *J. Biol. Chem., 192,* 733 (1951).

18. E. P. Tyner, C. Heidelberger, and G. A. Le Page, *Cancer Research, 13,* 186 (1953).

19. R. M. S. Smellie, W. M. McIndoe, and J. N. Davidson, *Biochem. et Biophys. Acta, 11,* 559 (1953).

20. P. Siekevitz, *J. Biol. Chem., 195,* 549 (1952).

21. V. Allfrey, M. N. Daly, and A. E. Mirsky, *J. Gen. Physiol., 37,* 157 (1953).

22. P. C. Zamecnik and E. B. Keller, *J. Biol. Chem., 209,* 337 (1954).

23. D. E. Green, *J. Cellular Comp. Physiol., 39,* suppl., 2, 75 (1952).

24. S. Brenner, *S. African J. Med. Sci., 12,* 53 (1947).

25. J. Brachet, *Chemical Embryology,* Interscience, New York, 1950.

26. T. Caspersson, *Cell Growth and Cell Function,* Norton, New York, 1950.

27. K. R. Porter, A. Claude, and E. F. Fullam, *J. Exptl. Med., 81,* 233 (1945).

28. A. Claude, K. R. Porter, and E. G. Pickels, *Cancer Research, 7,* 421 (1947).

29. K. R. Porter and F. L. Kallman, *Ann. N. Y. Acad. Sci., 54,* 882 (1952).

30. K. R. Porter, *J. Exptl. Med., 97,* 727 (1953).

31. A. Claude, *Harvey Lectures, 48,* 121 (1947–1948).

32. A. Claude and E. F. Fullam, *J. Exptl. Med., 83,* 499 (1946).

33. S. B. Newman, E. Borysko, and M. Swerdlow, *J. Research Natl. Bur. Standards, 43,* 183 (1949).

34. G. E. Palade, *J. Exptl. Med., 95,* 285 (1952).

35. K. R. Porter and J. Blum, *Anat. Record, 117,* 685 (1953).

36. F. S. Sjöstrand, *Experientia, 9,* 114 (1953).

37. W. Bernhard, A. Cautier, and C. Rouillier, *Arch. anat. micr. et morphol. exp., 43,* 236 (1954).

38. G. E. Palade, *J. Biophys. Biochem. Cytol., 2,* suppl., 85 (1956).

39. F. S. Sjöstrand, Electron microscopy of cells and tissues, in *Physical Techniques in Biological Research, III* (G. Oster and A. W. Pollister, editors), Academic Press, New York, 1956.

40. G. E. Palade and K. R. Porter, *J. Exptl. Med., 100,* 641 (1954).

41. G. E. Palade, *J. Biophys. Biochem. Cytol., 1,* 567 (1955).

42. S. L. Palay and G. E. Palade, *J. Biophys. Biochem. Cytol., 1,* 69 (1955).

43. G. E. Palade, *J. Biophys. Biochem. Cytol., 1,* 59 (1955).

44. G. E. Palade, *J. Applied Phys., 24,* 1419 (1953).

45. H. K. Schachman, A. B. Pardee, and R. Y. Stanier, *Arch. Biochem. Biophys., 38,* 245 (1952).

46. M. L. Petermann and M. G. Hamilton, *Cancer Research, 12,* 373 (1952).

47. M. L. Petermann, N. A. Mizen, and M. G. Hamilton, *Cancer Research, 13,* 372 (1953).

48. G. B. Chapman and J. Hillier, *J. Bacteriol., 66,* 362 (1953).

49. A. Birch Andersen, O. Maaløe, and F. S. Sjöstrand, *Biochim. Biophys. Acta, 12,* 395 (1953).

50. J. R. D. Bradfield, Organization of bacterial cytoplasm, in *Bacterial Anatomy,* University Press, Cambridge, 1956.

51. G. E. Palade and P. Siekevitz, *J. Biophys. Biochem. Cytol., 2,* 171 (1956).

52. A. J. Dalton and M. D. Felix, *Symposia Soc. Exptl. Biol., 10,* 148 (1957).

53. G. E. Palade and P. Siekevitz, *J. Biophys. Biochem. Cytol., 2,* 671 (1956).

54. P. Siekevitz and G. E. Palade, *Federation Proc., 17,* 311 (1958); *J. Biophys. Biochem. Cytol., 4* (in press) (1958).

55. J. W. Littlefield, E. B. Keller, J. Gross, and P. C. Zamecnik, *J. Biol. Chem., 217,* 111 (1955).

56. J. W. Littlefield and E. B. Keller, *J. Biol. Chem., 224,* 13 (1957).

57. P. Siekevitz and G. E. Palade, *J. Biophys. Biochem. Cytol., 4* (in press) (1958).

58. G. E. Palade, *J. Biophys. Biochem. Cytol., 2,* 417 (1956).

59. A. F. Howatson and A. W. Ham, *Can. J. Biochem. Physiol., 35,* 549 (1957).

60. H. A. Lund, A. E. Vatter, and J. B. Hanson, *J. Biophys. Biochem. Cytol., 4,* 87 (1958).

61. D. W. Fawcett and C. C. Selby, *J. Biophys. Biochem. Cytol., 4,* 63 (1958).

62. M. L. Petermann, M. G. Hamilton, and N. A. Mizen, *Cancer Research, 14,* 360 (1954).

63. F. C. Chao and H. K. Schachman, *Arch. Biochem. Biophys., 61,* 220 (1956).

64. P. O. Ts'o, J. Bonner, and J. Vinograd, *J. Biophys. Biochem. Cytol., 2,* 451 (1956).

65. M. L. Petermann and M. G. Hamilton, *J. Biol. Chem., 224,* 725 (1957).

66. E. L. Kuff, G. H. Hogeboom, and A. J. Dalton, *J. Biophys. Biochem. Cytol., 2,* 33 (1956).

67. J. Chauveau, Y. Moulé, and C. Rouillier, *Exptl. Cell Research, 13,* 398 (1957).

Fig. 1. The electron micrograph shows part of two adjacent exocrine cells in the pancreas of a guinea pig. The apposed membranes of the two cells appear obliquely sectioned at *cm*.

The basal region of one of these cells occupies the lower half of the figure and characteristically contains a few mitochondrial profiles (*m*) and numerous profiles of the endoplasmic reticulum (*rs*), which belong to the rough-surfaced type and show a certain amount of preferred orientation, i.e., are disposed in more or less parallel rows.

The apical region of the cell, in the upper part of the figure, is occupied by a few circular profiles of zymogen granules (*z*). Their dense content consists of stored digestive enzymes and enzyme precursors. Elements of the endoplasmic reticulum appear disposed at random among the zymogen granules. Part of the centrosphere region of the cell, with its characteristic clusters of smooth-surfaced vesicles, can be seen at *cs*.

A region similar to the lower right quarter of this figure appears in figure 2 at a higher magnification.

Specimen fixed for 2 hours at 0° C in 1 per cent OsO_4 in veronal acetate buffer, pH 7.6, containing ~5 per cent sucrose; embedded in *n* butyl methacrylate.

Magnification: 24,000.

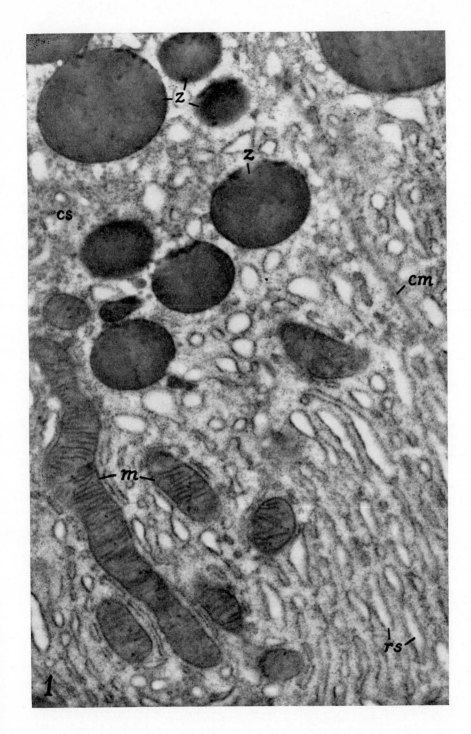

1

Fig. 2. The micrograph shows at a high magnification a small field in the basal region of a pancreatic exocrine cell (rat).

Parts of two mitochondrial profiles appear at *m;* the rest of the field is taken by numerous profiles of the endoplasmic reticulum (*rs*), most of which are of elongated form and appear disposed in parallel rows. In three dimensions many of these profiles correspond to relatively large but flat vesicles known as cisternae.

The membrane limiting the cavities of the reticulum appears as a dense, fine line (*n*) whenever sectioned normally, and as a less dense, poorly outlined band (*o*) when cut obliquely. In a few places the section has opened small windows (*f*) in the wall of the cisternae.

The membrane of the endoplasmic reticulum separates two distinct phases in the cytoplasm: one is represented by the light, homogeneous material enclosed in the cavities of the system (*c*); the other, by the surrounding cytoplasmic matrix (*mx*).

Numerous small, dense particles, $\sim$150 A in diameter, appear attached to the outer surface of the membrane limiting the cavities of the endoplasmic reticulum (*ap*). In addition to these attached particles, particles of comparable size and density occur apparently freely scattered in the cytoplasmic matrix (*fp*). Note, however, that many of these particles form short chains (arrows) anchored with one end among the attached particles.

Fixation: 24 hours at room temperature in 1 per cent OsO_4 in acetate veronal buffer, *p*H 7.6. As a result of the long fixation, part of the cytoplasmic matrix has been extracted and the profiles of the endoplasmic reticulum and the small, dense particles appear in better contrast.

Embedding: *n* butyl methacrylate.

Magnification: 50,000.

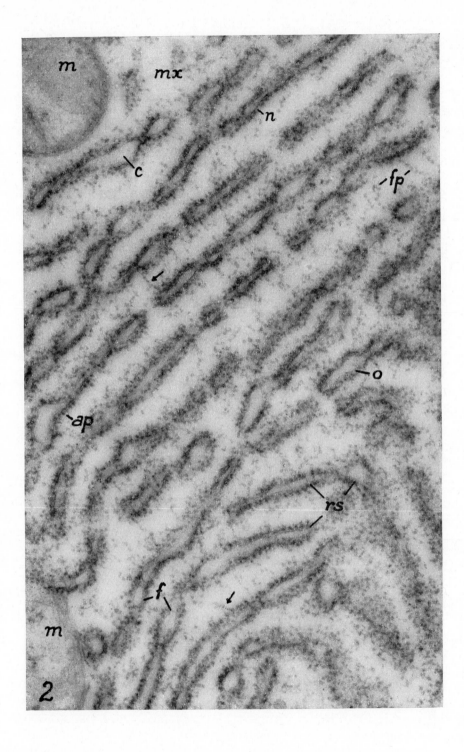

Fig. 3. The micrograph shows a small field in the basal region of a pancreatic exocrine cell which was damaged (cut open) during the trimming of the tissue block before fixation.

A comparison with figure 2 indicates that in the damaged cell the profiles of the endoplasmic reticulum have distended cavities and are predominantly circular. In three dimensions they correspond to spherical and oval vesicles. An enspherulation of this type is usually accompanied by a breaking-down of the system into a collection of isolated vesicles. Note that the vesicles are still aligned in more or less parallel rows.

The limiting membrane of the vesicles and its attached particles appear in normal section at *n*, and in oblique section at *o*. In this case there are few free particles left in the cytoplasmic matrix.

Fixation and embedding as for the specimen in figure 2.

Magnification: 50,000.

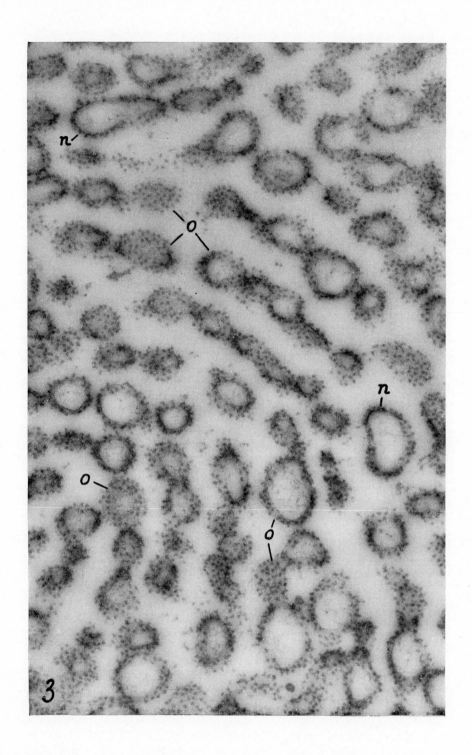

Fig. 4. Section through a microsome pellet isolated by differential centrifugation from a pancreatic brei (guinea pig) prepared in 0.88 M sucrose.

The microsomes are small, closed vesicles limited by a thin membrane which bears small ($\sim$150 A), dense particles attached to its outer surface. The apparent heterogeneity of the microsomal fraction is due primarily to sectioning. Some vesicles are seen in median section (mv_1) and therefore clearly display their normally sectioned membrane and their attached particles. Other vesicles are cut medially (mv_2) and show obliquely sectioned, poorly defined membranes. Finally, in lateral sections (mv_3), the cavity of the microsomes cannot be seen, and their particle-studded membrane appears in full-face view.

The structural details described indicate that the microsomes are derived (by fragmentation) from the rough-surfaced part of the endoplasmic reticulum. A comparison with figure 2 suggests that the fragmentation occurs spontaneously when the cell membrane is ruptured during tissue grinding.

Note that the microsomal content varies widely in density from light (mv_1) to medium (mv_4) and high (mv_5). A ruptured microsomal vesicle ($m\dot{v}_6$) contains the equivalent of an intracisternal granule.

Fixation: 2 hours at 0° C in 2 per cent OsO_4 in 30 per cent (0.88 M) sucrose.

Embedding: n butyl methacrylate.

Magnification: 72,000.

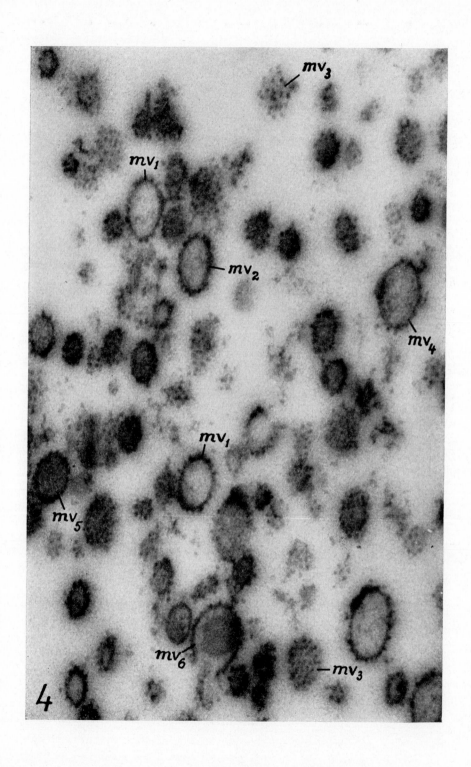

Fig. 5. Small field in a microsomal pellet (guinea pig) prepared like the specimen in figure 4.

A few microsomal vesicles appear in median (mv_1), medial (mv_2), and lateral (mv_3) section. The particles attached to the outer surface of the limiting membrane (arrows) display their characteristic small size ($\sim$150 A) and high density.

Fig. 6. Small field in a pellet obtained by differentially centrifuging a microsomal suspension (like the one in figure 5) treated with Na deoxycholate (0.1 per cent, pH 7.2).

The pellet consists of dense particles, $\sim$150 A in diameter, which frequently occur in chains (arrows) or in clusters. Their general morphology suggests that they are particles detached from the microsomes as a result of the solubilization of the microsomal membrane by deoxycholate.

Both pellets were fixed and embedded like the specimen in figure 4.
Magnification: 120,000 for both figures.

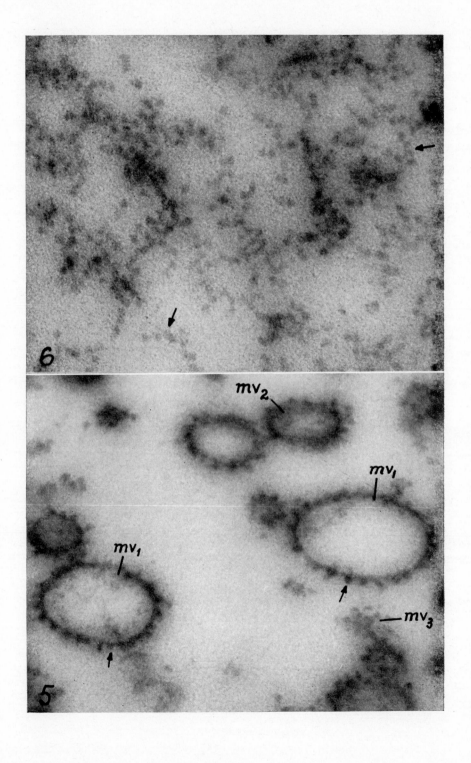

Fig. 7. Pellet of a second postmicrosomal fraction obtained by differential centrifugation (16 hours at 105,000g) from a pancreatic brei (guinea pig) prepared in 0.88 M sucrose.

The fraction consists of small (~150 A), dense particles which occur either isolated or in chains (arrows). They are assumed to be the "free" particles of the cytoplasmic matrix. Fixation and embedding as for the specimen in figure 4.

Magnification: 160,000.

7

The Influence of Conditions of Culture on Certain Soluble Macromolecular Components of *Escherichia coli*

S. DAGLEY   J. SYKES

Department of Biochemistry, University of Leeds, England

Schachman, Pardee, and Stanier [1] used the analytical ultracentrifuge to examine soluble extracts prepared from various bacterial species disrupted by different methods, and they showed the presence in all extracts of three major components having sedimentation coefficients (uncorrected) of about 40, 29, and 5 S. Other workers (Siegel, Singer, and Wildman [2] and Billen and Volkin [3]) have obtained ultracentrifuge patterns in substantial agreement. For the strain of *Escherichia coli* we have used, a typical "basic" pattern is seen in figure 3a, where the boundaries, reading from left to right, sediment respectively at 40, 29, and 20 S followed by a large, slow-moving peak which, on centrifuging for longer periods, resolves into two peaks of 8 and 5 S. Although the ultracentrifuge has revealed a common pattern of macromolecules, however, the ever-increasing range of enzymes shown to be induced in bacteria supports the assertion that they are "the most plastic of living material" (Stephenson [4]); and accordingly we have tried to find out whether changes in their environment have any influence upon the ultracentrifuge pattern.

This work may be divided into two parts. First, we examined the basic ultracentrifuge pattern for modifications that might result from growth of the cells on different sources of carbon; and we also determined rates of sedimentation of certain enzymes, some of which were induced by addition of substrates to cultures, in order to decide whether any of them appeared to be associated with macromolecules revealed by ultracentrifugal analysis. The second series of experiments was concerned with factors affecting the concentration of the 40 S component inside the living cells.

SEDIMENTATION OF ENZYMES

E. coli cells were usually grown without aeration in media containing 0.13 *M* KH$_2$PO$_4$ brought to *p*H 7 with NaOH; growth in 0.01 *M* glucose was then limited entirely by exhaustion of the source of carbon, and changes in *p*H were negligible. The medium was completed by addition, per liter, of 0.2 g MgSO$_4$·7H$_2$O and either 1 g (NH$_4$)$_2$SO$_4$ (for a "mineral salts" medium) or 10 g Difco bactopeptone. Extracts were prepared from cells disintegrated in the Hughes [5] bacterial press without abrasive; soluble material was extracted by stirring with 0.066 *M* phosphate buffer, *p*H 7, and cell debris was removed by centrifuging for 15 minutes at 102,000*g*. The protein content of the extracts was then determined by the biuret colorimetric method and adjusted to 10 mg protein/ml by addition of buffer. This solution could be stored at 0° C for 24 hours before examination, but freezing and thawing caused alterations in ultracentrifuge patterns. When glucose was the source of carbon, irrespective of whether it was limiting for growth or supplied in excess, or whether (NH$_4$)$_2$SO$_4$ or peptone was the nitrogen source, cells in mid-logarithmic phase gave patterns with boundaries that sedimented at about 40, 29, 20, and 8 S.

It was only when cell division had ceased for several hours that modifications could be seen, namely, a reduction in the size of the 40 S peak and the appearance of a small 13 S peak. By contrast, when cells grown on glucose were incubated in a lactose growth medium, a 13 S boundary was observed for actively dividing cells. When lactose was utilized as sole carbon source in a mineral salts medium there was a lag of 80 minutes before cell division began, but the β-galactosidase activity of the culture was increasing in this period and a trace of the 13 S component appeared in that time. When peptone was the nitrogen source, β-galactosidase was synthesized much faster and the lag preceding cell division was only 20 minutes.

Ultracentrifuge patterns for extracts from these cells are shown in figure 1, where, since photographs were taken at 32 minutes, the 40 S boundaries have already sedimented. After incubation with lactose for 100 minutes, peaks of 29, 20, and 13 S are well defined. Extracts from cells at this stage of growth on glucose show only 29 and 20 S boundaries in addition to 8 S after centrifuging for 32 minutes, the trace of 13 S component in the initial stationary phase culture being lost during cell division. When cells were adapted to utilize galactose and D-xylose as sources of carbon, boundaries that sedimented at about 13 S also appeared; and they were visible in extracts containing the induced enzyme citratase (Dagley and Sykes [6]).

A correlation may therefore be suggested between the appearance of 13 S components and the induction of certain enzymes, including those that may be developed by glucose-grown cells as they remain in the stationary phase in the presence of accumulated products of metabolism. The significance of such a correlation, however, is not evident. It is possible, for example, that 13 S

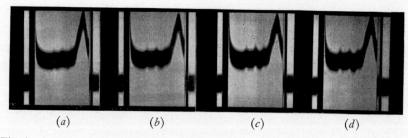

(a)   (b)   (c)   (d)

Fig. 1. Patterns at 32 minutes and 187,000g for extracts from *E. coli* during growth in lactose medium. Cells were harvested from: (*a*) a stationary-phase glucose mineral salts culture; (*b*) lactose medium when in early logarithmic phase, 30 minutes after transfer from (*a*); (*c*) 100 minutes after transfer; (*d*) after 160 minutes. Sedimentation is to the left, and visible peaks have sedimentation coefficients of 29, 20, 13, and 8 S. In each pattern the 40 S boundary has already sedimented.

components might have some general significance in enzyme induction processes, or, alternatively, that the actual enzyme molecules are synthesized in amounts sufficient to affect the ultracentrifuge patterns and that, by coincidence, the molecules of those we have studied are all of the size (and shape) to sediment at about 13 S.

Data tending to favor the second suggestion were obtained by following the sedimentation of enzyme activities in extracts. For these measurements, the rotor was allowed to come to rest after a field of 187,000g had been maintained for a definite time interval, and the cell was carefully removed. By means of a syringe it was possible to withdraw almost the whole of the supernatant without disturbing the pellet deposited in the cell. The activity remaining in the supernatant was then determined, and the sequence of operations was repeated for a different length of centrifugation so that a graph could be constructed to relate duration of spin to supernatant activity.

The enzymes assayed were arginine, lysine, and glutamate decarboxylases (Gale [7]) for extracts from cells grown in media containing 2 per cent glucose and 1 per cent peptone with addition of the corresponding amino acids; citratase using the media and methods of Dagley and Sykes [6]; and the β-galactosidase (Lederberg [8]) of cells grown at the expense of lactose. The constitutive enzymes of the TCA cycle, malic and isocitric dehydrogenases, fumarase and aconitase, present in extracts of cells grown in mineral salts media with limiting glucose, were also assayed by the spectrophotometric methods used by Englesberg and colleagues [9, 10].

In figure 2 it is seen that centrifuging for about 90 minutes removed all the citratase, β-galactosidase, and glutamic decarboxylase of extracts. This is the time taken to sediment the 13 S boundary. Lysine and arginine decarboxylases sedimented faster, at about the speed of the 20 S boundary. Malic and isocitric dehydrogenase activity moved much more slowly, and fumarase and aconitase appreciably slower than 13 S. The behavior of the four TCA-cycle enzymes is in agreement with the view that they were present in these extracts as individual molecules, since an approximate molecular weight of 40,000 has been assigned to malic dehydrogenase (Wolfe and Nielands [11]), of 64,000 to iso-citric dehydrogenase (Dixon and Moyle [12]), and 204,000 to fumarase (Massey [13]; Cecil and Ogston [14]). If an estimate of 700,000 is taken as the molecular weight of β-galactosidase (Cohn [15]), the enzyme is certainly no smaller than the 13 S component and its synthesis during adaptation to lactose might well result in an addition to the pattern in this region. If this is also true for the other induced enzymes it is surprising that they appear to be synthesized in such quantity and that the molecules are so large that they sediment between 13 and 20 S.

It is sometimes stated that a number of enzymes are located in the 40 S component, but this is not so for the activities we have investigated. In this connection, observations on another system studied in these laboratories are relevant (Callely, Dagley, and Hodgson [16]). Extracts have been prepared from a vibrio which catalyze the oxidation of octanoate and other fatty acids to acetate, apparently by the reactions of the fatty acid spiral (Lynen and Ochoa [17]). If there are associations of related biochemical activities upon the 40 S particle analogous to those present in various particles from higher organisms, they might well be sought here; but in fact the component may be removed from these extracts with little diminution of the over-all rate of oxidation.

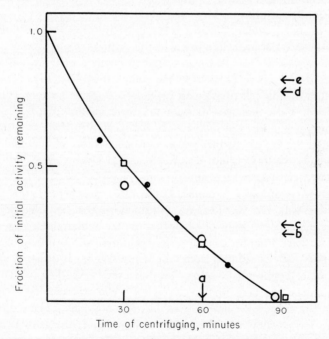

Fig. 2. Sedimentation of enzymes at 187,000*g*. Experimental points for: β-galactosidase, solid circle; citratase, square; glutamic decarboxylase, open circle. Arrow *a* shows time when no lysine or arginine decarboxylase remained; and *b, c, d,* and *e* show levels of supernatant activities after 90 minutes for fumarase, aconitase, isocitric dehydrogenase, and malic dehydrogenase, respectively.

THE 40 S COMPONENT

Variations in the concentration of the 40 S component due to cultural changes were far greater than for 13 S. Cells grown in peptone contained higher concentrations of the 40 S component than those at a corresponding phase of growth in mineral salts media, and for both types of medium the concentration increased during cell division and decreased in the stationary phase. Since the 40 S component carries most of the RNA of *E. coli* (Schachman et al. [1]), these observations agree with Wade and Morgan [18], who found a higher RNA content for dividing than for resting cells; but we have never examined extracts of cells harvested from stationary-phase cultures that were entirely devoid of 40, 29, or 20 S components although we adopted the same extraction procedures as these authors in several experiments. Cells that had remained 2 hours in a stationary culture were not distinguishable from those late in logarithmic growth; and a significant reduction in the 40 S component could only be seen after 8 hours.

The most striking effect observed was the disappearance of the 40 S boundary when cells were resuspended in phosphate buffer of the same strength ($0.13\ M$) as that in the growth medium from which they were harvested. Apparently no permanent damage is done to the cells by this treatment because, on addition to the buffer of glucose, Mg^{++} and $(NH_4)_2SO_4$ or peptone, growth occurs with little or no lag period. These observations are illustrated in figure 3 with patterns of extracts from cells grown to the stationary phase in mineral salts medium (*a*), which were then transferred to peptone medium and examined in mid-logarithmic phase (*b*) and at the end of this phase (*c*). The augmentation of 40 S during cell division in peptone is evident; and, in (*c*), 29 S has also increased. Cells that gave pattern (*c*) were incubated for 30 minutes in 0.13 M phosphate, and most of the 40 S disappeared to leave two small peaks of 43 and 40 S (*d*); on further incubation only traces of material remained that sedimented in this region (*e*). Peptone and glucose were now added to the suspended cells; growth resumed, and (*f*) gives the pattern after 1 hour.

Some of the conditions for stabilizing the 40 S component within whole cells were investigated. Dr. A. Tissieres informed us that its disappearance depended on the concentration of phosphate in the buffer used to suspend the cells, and we have found a considerable diminution of the rate of loss of 40 S when the phosphate is reduced from 0.13 M to 0.066 M. It does not appear that the effect of orthophosphate is specific, however, since disappearance of the 40 S component has been shown for whole cells resuspended in potassium chloride of the same ionic strength as 0.13 M phosphate. The importance of magnesium ions is shown by the results of figure 4. If the growth medium is complete except for addition of Mg^{++}, 40 S is lost (fig. 4*b*). On addition of Mg^{++}, 40 S is stabilized and cell division may begin; but Mg^{++} may stabilize this component even in cells that are not able to divide because the source of energy has been omitted (fig. 4*c*). Wade and Morgan [18] have shown an association

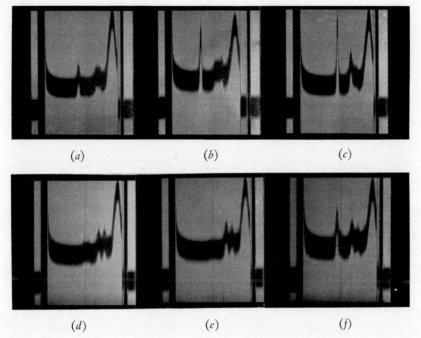

Fig. 3. Patterns after 16 minutes' centrifuging at 187,000g for extracts from cells, in stationary-phase glucose mineral salts culture (a); in mid-logarithmic phase after transfer to glucose peptone medium (b); in late logarithmic phase in this medium (c); after incubation with 0.13 M phosphate buffer, pH 7, (d) for 30 minutes and (e) for 120 minutes. The volume of buffer for resuspension was the same as that of the culture from which the cells were taken. On addition of glucose and peptone to the suspension the cells grew, and pattern (f) was given after 1 hour.

of magnesium ions with an ultracentrifuge fraction that contains the 40 S component, and, drawing attention to the observation of Webb [19] that bacteria may synthesize protein but may not divide when there is a deficiency of magnesium, they make the stimulating suggestion that the RNA in this fraction is directly concerned with the cell-division process.

Without further study we cannot conclude that the stability of the 40 S component in whole cells is determined solely by the concentrations of Mg^{++} and other inorganic ions in the medium. Thus it appears that when cells are grown in a rich peptone medium they are less readily depleted of 40 S than when grown in mineral salts; and, in our studies of β-galactosidase development during the lag in cell division in a lactose mineral salts medium, we observed a reduction in this component although the magnesium content of the culture was normal. It is therefore possible that other factors concerned with the metabolism of the cell may also control the stabilization or degradation of the 40 S macromolecule.

When a cell-free extract was diluted, or the buffer concentration used in its

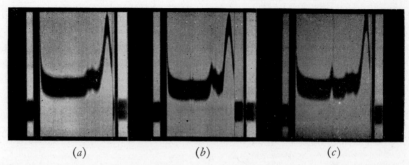

(a)   (b)   (c)

Fig. 4. Patterns, after 16 minutes' centrifuging at 187,000g, for extracts from cells grown in a glucose mineral salts medium and then resuspended in solutions containing 1 g $(NH_4)_2SO_4$ per liter of 0.13 M phosphate buffer, pH 7, with no further addition (a); addition of 0.01 M glucose (b); addition of 0.2 g $MgSO_4 \cdot 7H_2O$ per liter (c). Cells were incubated for 90 minutes in the same volume of solution as that from which they were harvested.

preparation was increased, the proportion of 40 S relative to the other components was reduced. The patterns shown in figure 5 suggest a split of 40 S macromolecules into 29 and 20 S on dilution, favored by high phosphate concentration. Thus, no 40 S boundary was visible in 0.2 M phosphate: the leading peaks in the extract which contained 7.5 mg protein/ml sedimented at measured (uncorrected) speeds of 27 and 20 S respectively; and from their in-

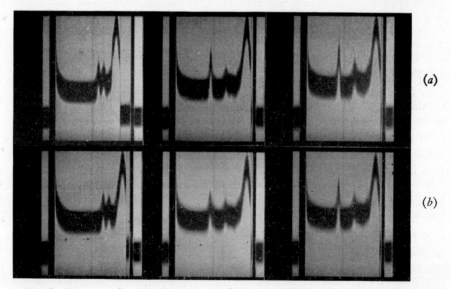

(a)

(b)

Fig. 5. Patterns, after 16 minutes' centrifuging at 187,000g, for extracts prepared in three strengths of phosphate buffer. Extract concentrations were: 10 mg protein/ml (a); 7.5 mg protein/ml (b). Sedimentation to the left; in 0.066 M and 0.04 M phosphate, boundaries of 40, 29, 20, and 8 S are visible. The three photographs of either series were taken at the same schlieren angle; but an adjustment was made between series to provide comparable areas for the 8 S peak.

creased areas it appears that the components forming these boundaries may contain the material that appears as 40 S at lower phosphate concentrations. In 0.066 *M* phosphate, the leading boundary sedimented at 40 S followed by 26 S and 19 S at 10 mg protein/ml, but there was dissociation of the 40 S component at 7.5 mg protein/ml. In 0.04 *M* phosphate, 40 S was stable at both concentrations of extract. It is of interest that concentrations of phosphate above 0.06 *M*, but not below, effect a loss of the 40 S components whether they are inside the cells or in extracts isolated from them. This supports the evidence of Roberts et al. [20] that the phosphate concentration inside *E. coli* does not differ greatly from that outside. The final results of disintegration of the 40 S component, however, are not the same in whole cells as in extracts, for 29 and 20 S components appear to be the main disintegration products in extracts, whereas in whole cells these peaks are not strongly augmented. It is possible that the initial split of 40 S is to give 29 and 20 S components and that in whole cells the process goes further to produce lower-molecular-weight diffusible material.

We are grateful to the Medical Research Council for their financial support of this work.

REFERENCES

1. H. K. Schachman, A. B. Pardee, and R. Y. Stanier, *Arch. Biochem. Biophys.,* *38,* 245 (1952).

2. A. Siegel, S. J. Singer, and S. G. Wildman, *Arch. Biochem. Biophys.,* *41,* 278 (1952).

3. D. Billen and E. Volkin, *J. Bacteriol.,* *67,* 191 (1954).

4. M. Stephenson, *Bacterial Metabolism,* 3d ed., p. 311, Longmans, Green and Company, London, 1949.

5. D. E. Hughes, *Brit. J. Exptl. Pathol.,* *32,* 97 (1951).

6. S. Dagley and J. Sykes, *Arch. Biochem. Biophys.,* *62,* 338 (1956).

7. E. F. Gale, *Advances in Enzymol.,* *6,* 1 (1946).

8. J. Lederberg, *J. Bacteriol.,* *60,* 381 (1950).

9. E. Englesberg, J. B. Levy, and A. Gibor, *J. Bacteriol.,* *68,* 178 (1954).

10. E. Englesberg and J. B. Levy, *J. Bacteriol.,* *69,* 418 (1955).

11. R. Wolfe and J. Nielands, *J. Biol. Chem.,* *221,* 61 (1956).

12. M. Dixon and J. Moyle, *Biochem. J.,* *63,* 548 (1956).

13. V. Massey, *Biochem. J.,* *51,* 490 (1952).

14. R. Cecil and A. G. Ogston, *Biochem. J.,* *51,* 494 (1952).

15. M. Cohn, *Bacteriol. Revs.,* *21,* 140 (1957).

16. A. G. Callely, S. Dagley, and B. Hodgson, *Biochem. J.,* *66,* 47P (1957).

17. F. Lynen and S. Ochoa, *Biochim. et Biophys. Acta,* *12,* 299 (1953).

18. H. E. Wade and D. M. Morgan, *Biochem. J.,* *65,* 321 (1957).

19. M. Webb, *J. Gen. Microbiol.,* *3,* 410 (1949).

20. R. B. Roberts, P. H. Abelson, D. B. Cowie, E. T. Bolton, and R. J. Britten, *Studies of Biosynthesis in Escherichia coli,* Carnegie Inst. Wash. Publ. 607, Washington, D. C., 1955.

8

Physicochemical and Metabolic Studies on Rat Liver Ribonucleoprotein[1]

MARY L. PETERMANN   MARY G. HAMILTON

M. EARL BALIS   KUMUD SAMARTH[2]   PAULINE PECORA

*Sloan-Kettering Institute for Cancer Research
and Sloan-Kettering Division, Cornell University Medical College*

The presence in uninfected tissues of particles with sedimentation constants of about 75 S has long been known to virologists [1]. Similar macromolecules have been found in tumors (Kahler and Bryan [2]). We first observed them in spleen [3], and later in liver, pancreas, and various tumors [4]. They are now known to be ribonucleoproteins (RNP) [5]. Ultracentrifugal patterns of these RNPs show a number of boundaries. Their sedimentation coefficients are so strongly dependent on concentration that we have denoted them by letters, such as B, C, and E, rather than identifying them by their sedimentation constants at infinite dilution. B has a sedimentation constant of 78 S, C of about 62 S, and E of 46 S, corresponding roughly with the S80, S60, and S40 boundaries found in nucleoproteins from microorganisms.

In general, where we find a large amount of nucleoprotein B, as in pancreas and normal liver [4], the electron microscopists find most of the granules attached to endoplasmic reticulum [6]; but where we find increased amounts of C and E, as in liver tumors [4], the electron microscopists find granules not attached to reticulum [7]. We therefore wanted to see whether a large microsome fraction, containing only RNP bound to endoplasmic reticulum, contained only B, while a small microsome or ultramicrosome fraction containing free RNP particles was rich in C and E.

[1] The authors wish to acknowledge the assistance of the Atomic Energy Commission (Contract no. AT (30-1)—910), and the National Cancer Institute of the United States Public Health Service (grants nos. C-2329 and CY-3190).

[2] Visiting research fellow.

We prepared such fractions by differential centrifugation at 78,000g in 0.79 M sucrose. The whole microsome fraction was centrifuged for 5 hours. The large-microsome fraction was centrifuged for only 50 minutes, in order to sediment only large fragments of endoplasmic reticulum. From this supernatant the small-microsome fraction was sedimented for 5 hours. Each fraction was washed by resedimentation in 0.79 M sucrose containing 5×10^{-4} M K_2HPO_4 and KH_2PO_4, and 5×10^{-4} M $MgCl_2$ to preserve the RNP [8], and finally was suspended in this same buffer without the sucrose, or in water, to a RNP concentration of about 5 mg/ml. For ultracentrifugal analysis each sample was diluted with 0.2 volume of a fivefold concentrated buffer. Two sets of analyses carried out in 0.1 M $KHCO_3$ are shown in figure 1. When a mere trace of magnesium is present, as in the upper row, the RNP from the large microsomes is chiefly B, with only small amounts of C and E. The small microsomes, however, do show considerable amounts of C and E. With 0.0024 M magnesium, in the bottom row, all preparations show less C and E, but the same relationship is retained—there is more C and E in the small microsomes than in the large ones. The whole microsome fraction falls in between, as one would expect. Varying the pH or the concentrations of monobasic and dibasic ions gives an assortment of patterns, but there is always more C and E in the extracts of the small microsomes.

Whether any of the RNP in the small-microsome fraction is really "free" in the liver cell, however, is difficult to determine. In extracts made in water or the dilute phosphate-magnesium buffer, at pH 7, no RNP boundaries are seen in the ultracentrifuge. They appear when the pH is raised to 8.0 or the ionic strength is increased. Since the state of the particles is so dependent on their ionic environment, they will have to be studied in buffers which approximate

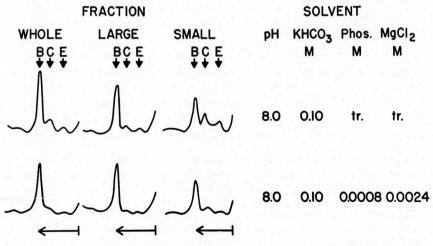

Fig. 1. Ultracentrifugal patterns of RNP extracted from microsomal fractions. The pictures were taken after 14 minutes at 37,020 rpm.

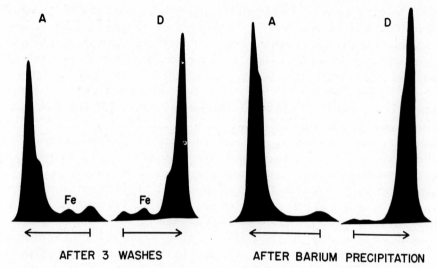

Fig. 2. Electrophoretic patterns of purified RNP in 0.10 M KHCO$_3$, pH 8.2, containing 0.001 M MgCl$_2$. Pictures taken after 60 minutes at 5.2 volts/cm. The left-hand patterns show RNP that had been washed three times. The right-hand patterns show the same material after removal of the ferritin. (See text.)

the ionic composition of the liver cell before any conclusions can be drawn.[3]

Most of our recent work has been carried out on purified RNP [9]. The microsomes are disrupted with deoxycholate, and the RNP is purified by alternate cycles of high- and low-speed centrifugation. Recently we have made some improvements in the procedure. The livers do not have to be perfused. The addition of penicillin (100 units/ml) to all the solutions increases the stability.[4] Instead of washing with calf-liver dialysate we now use the potassium phosphate–magnesium chloride buffer; its pH is about 7. The washed RNP still shows about 5 per cent of ferritin on electrophoretic analysis (fig. 2). This can be removed by precipitating the RNP with 0.005 M barium acetate and redissolving it by dialysis against 5×10^{-4} M K$_2$HPO$_4$, KH$_2$PO$_4$, and MgSO$_4$ (fig. 2).

We have carried out extensive studies of the stability of purified RNP. Like the crude microsomal extracts, the purified RNP is very sensitive to pH, ionic strength, and dibasic and monobasic cations. Figure 3 shows the effect of magnesium in the presence of 0.1 M NaHCO$_3$. Fresh RNP looks like the third

[3] Recently we have prepared large- and small-microsome fractions by sedimentation in 0.20 M sucrose, and resuspended them in water at pH 7.1 without washing. On ultracentrifugal analysis sizable C and E boundaries were observed in the small-microsome fraction, although none were apparent in the large-microsome fraction.

[4] The purification of the RNP requires about 3 days; although the preparation is kept cold, unless penicillin or sterile technique is used the RNP has an odor like that of spoiled meat. This may be due to cadaverine produced from N-terminal lysine by bacterial lysine decarboxylase; after treatment of the RNP with dinitrofluorobenzene and acid hydrolysis, the only DNP amino acid detectable is lysine.

picture down, chiefly B. After dialysis overnight against bicarbonate containing 0.005 M $MgCl_2$ the RNP is unchanged. With less magnesium, as shown
in the two upper pictures, it dissociates; with more magnesium, as shown in
the bottom row, the B boundary gets smaller, because the RNP has begun to
aggregate and precipitate out.

In the purified RNP we found 40 per cent RNA on a dry-weight basis [9].
Similar values have been found for purified RNPs from yeast [10] and pea
seedlings [11], again on a dry-weight basis. When RNA is compared with
protein nitrogen, on the other hand, we and many other workers find values
for RNA of 50 to 60 per cent. Some of this discrepancy is probably caused by
lipid, which contributes more to the dry weight than to the nitrogen. Some of
it, however, seems to occur because hot 5 per cent trichloroacetic acid extracts
some other nitrogen besides that in the RNA. With 10, 15, and 20 per cent
trichloroacetic acid we still find extra nitrogen in the extracts.

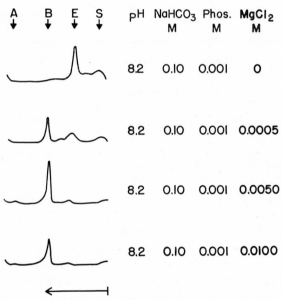

Fig. 3. The effect of magnesium on the stability of purified RNP. Ultracentrifugal
patterns were obtained after 14 minutes at 37,020 rpm.

We have carried out a number of metabolic studies on purified RNP containing about 4 per cent ferritin. Figure 4 shows the incorporation of glycine-
1-C^{14} into adenine and peptide glycine. The upper row shows the time course
of the incorporation in normal male rats. Fifteen minutes after the injection
of the isotope, by tail vein, the specific activity of the acid-soluble adenine of
the liver was quite high, whereas that of the adenine in the purified RNP was
still very low, and, although it increased very slowly with time, it was still low
at 17 hours. The specific activity of the liver nucleoprotein glycine was highest

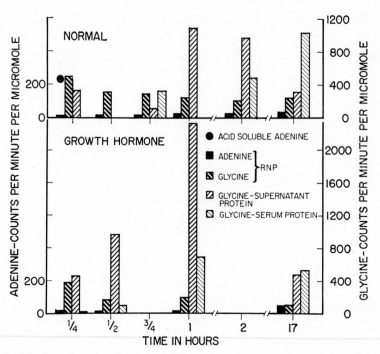

Fig. 4.   The incorporation of glycine-1-C^{14} into the adenine and glycine of rat liver RNP, and into "supernatant" and serum proteins (see text).

at 15 minutes and then dropped off. The glycine of the liver supernatant proteins, plus the microsomal lipoproteins soluble in deoxycholate, reached a maximum between 1 and 2 hours, and then fell. The glycine of the serum proteins increased very slowly, and was highest at 17 hours. Similar results have been obtained with labeled adenine and methionine as tracers.

The lower row shows the results obtained on rats pretreated with bovine growth hormone, 410 µg per rat per day, for 2 weeks. There was no effect on the RNP adenine, but the effects on the three protein fractions were marked. Everything seemed to have been speeded up. The nucleoprotein glycine activity dropped more rapidly; the liver supernatant activity rose more steeply; and the serum proteins apparently reached a maximum at some time before 17 hours, and then declined again.

These results illustrate, first, the lack of correspondence in the extents of isotope incorporation into the RNA and the total protein glycine of the RNP, and, second, the effect of growth hormone, which speeded up the incorporation of glycine into protein without any change in the rate at which the particle RNA became labeled. From these observations we conclude that, at least in rat liver, the total RNA of the RNP cannot be functioning as an active template.

REFERENCES

1. A. R. Taylor, D. G. Sharp, and B. Woodhall, *Science, 97,* 226 (1943).

2. H. Kahler and W. R. Bryan, *J. Natl. Cancer Inst., 4,* 37 (1943–1944).

3. M. L. Petermann and M. G. Hamilton, *Cancer Research, 12,* 373 (1952).

4. M. L. Petermann, N. A. Mizen, and M. G. Hamilton, *Cancer Research, 16,* 620 (1956).

5. M. L. Petermann, M. G. Hamilton, and N. A. Mizen, *Cancer Research, 14,* 360 (1954).

6. G. E. Palade, *J. Biophys. Biochem. Cytol., 1,* 59 (1955).

7. A. F. Howatson and A. W. Ham, *Cancer Research, 15,* 62 (1955).

8. F.-C. Chao, *Arch. Biochem. Biophys., 70,* 426 (1957).

9. M. L. Petermann and M. G. Hamilton, *J. Biol. Chem., 224,* 725 (1957).

10. F.-C. Chao and H. K. Schachman, *Arch. Biochem. Biophys., 61,* 220 (1956).

11. P. O. P. T'so, J. Bonner, and J. Vinograd, *J. Biophys. Biochem. Cytol., 2,* 451 (1956).

Ultracentrifugal Studies of Microsomes from Starving, Nonproliferating, and Proliferating Yeast

JAMES K. ASHIKAWA

Donner Laboratory of Biophysics and Medical Physics
University of California, Berkeley

In the decade since Claude's successful isolation of microsomes from liver and other tissue homogenates by differential centrifugation [1, 2], considerable progress has been made toward elucidating their biochemical and morphological characteristics. The microsomal "ribonucleoprotein" particles isolated from bacterial cells and from plant and animal tissues are rich in ribonucleic acid [3–10]. In electron-microscopic observations these microsomal particles, either isolated or in intact plant and animal cells, appear as spherical particles with diameters ranging from 100 to 400 A. They occur either bound to the endoplasmic reticulum or freely dispersed in the cytoplasmic matrix [7–14].

There are interesting studies indicating that microsomes may be actively involved in protein and lipid synthesis [5, 15, 16]. In vivo [17–20] and in vitro studies [15, 20, 21] have shown that labeled amino acids are preferentially incorporated into the microsomal proteins, suggesting synthetic activity.

Since these microsome particles appear to be functional organelles in both plant and animal cells, it is highly probable that their physicochemical properties will be altered by varying the physiological state of the cell. Preliminary studies of microsomes isolated from starving, nonproliferating, and proliferating yeast cells have shown that several new ribonucleoprotein particles appear during cell division [22, 23]. This paper presents further evidence thereon.

EXPERIMENTAL PROCEDURE AND RESULTS

Haploid yeast cells (*Saccharomyces cerevisiae* strain S. C. 7) aerobically cultured for 24 hours at 30° C in yeast extract and dextrose (YED 1:2 per cent) were harvested and washed twice with sterile distilled water. Aliquots of cells were then suspended in nitrogen-deficient medium (4 per cent dextrose : $M/60$ KH$_2$PO$_4$:3/60 M NaH$_2$PO$_4$) and aerated for 48 to 72 hours at 30° C. During this nitrogen starvation, the buffered dextrose medium in some of the cultures was changed every 12 hours. At the end of starvation, the cells were centrifuged and rewashed twice with sterile distilled water. Approximately 6 gram aliquots of wet cells were suspended in 2-liter flasks containing 1500 ml YED (1:2 per cent) and induced to grow aerobically at 30° for varying time intervals. The growth curve of the cells and the corresponding bud counts for the first 26 hours are shown in figure 1. The yeast cells were then harvested at different times, and microsomal particles were isolated according to Wolfe [23]. Cells hand-ground with 100-grid Carborundum in mortar and pestle at 0° C were extracted with several volumes of solvent (0.00125 M KH$_2$PO$_4$–K$_2$HPO$_4$ 3:7,

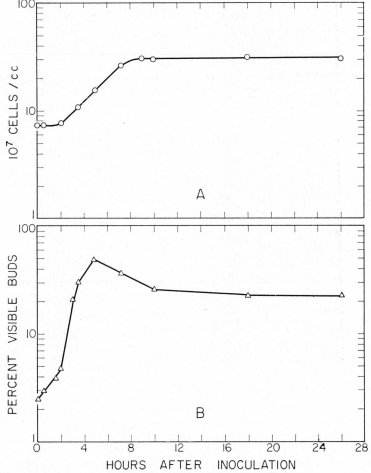

Fig. 1. Relationship of budding to growth of yeast cells. (*a*) Growth curve of 48-hour nitrogen-starved yeast cells aerobically cultured at 30° C in YED (1:2 per cent). (*b*) Curve correlating percentage of visible buds to corresponding growth stages.

0.001 M MgCl$_2$, and 0.01 M KCl). After vacuum filtration through celite filter-aid, the microsomes were sedimented from the filtrate by ultracentrifugation in the preparative ultracentrifuge (Spinco Model L) at 114,000g (40,000 rpm) for 1 hour. The translucent microsomal pellets isolated from yeast cells in different growth stages were carefully redissolved in the buffered solvent and analyzed in the analytical ultracentrifuge (Spinco Model E) at 200,000g. Figure 2 shows

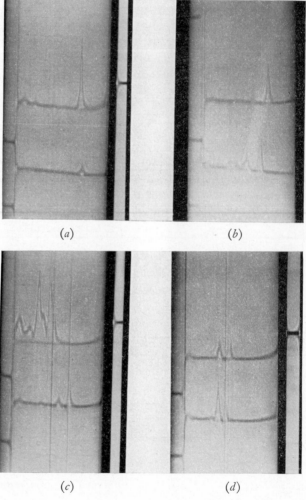

(a)   (b)

(c)   (d)

Fig. 2. Sedimentation photographs of microsome particles from yeast-cell extracts 6 minutes after up to speed (UTS) at 200,000g in the analytical ultracentrifuge (Spinco Model E). (*a*) *Top:* Cell extract from 48-hour nitrogen-starved cells corresponding to the inoculum cells at time 0. *Bottom:* Extract from nitrogen-starved cells 1.5 hours after cells given utilizable nitrogen. (*b*) *Top:* After 3 hours. *Bottom:* After 5 hours. (*c*) *Top:* 10 × concentrated extract from nitrogen-starved cells 7 hours after cells given utilizable nitrogen. *Bottom:* Extract from nitrogen-starved cells 10 hours after cells given utilizable nitrogen. (*d*) *Top:* After 26 hours. *Bottom:* After 52 hours.

the changes in the sedimentation pattern which indicate the appearance of new microsomal particles [22, 23]. During the lag phase when less than 3 per cent of the cells have visible buds, only the 80 S component (α peak in fig. 3) is present in the ultracentrifuge pattern of cytoplasmic extract. As the cells begin to proliferate and enter the log phase of growth (40 to 50 per cent visible buds), four new microsomal components (β, γ, δ, and ε peaks in fig. 3) appear in the cell extracts. From log growth phase through stationary phase, the only change in the sedimentation pattern appears to be in the ratio of these components.

Cell starvation is first evidenced by a decrease in the stability of the microsomes, which is indicated by the presence of polymerized material that sedi-

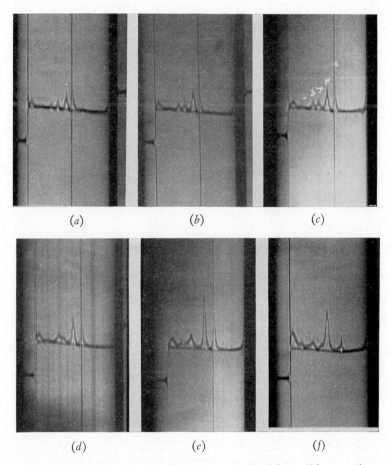

Fig. 3. Sedimentation photographs of microsomes isolated from 48-hour stationary-phase cells 6 minutes after UTS at 200,000g. (a) Yeast extract suspended in phosphate buffer (0.00125 M KH$_2$PO$_4$–K$_2$HPO$_4$ 3:7, 0.001 M MgCl$_2$, and 0.01 M KCl) at 4° C for 1 day. (b) Yeast extract suspended in phosphate buffer at 4° C for 2 days. (c) After 7 days. (d) After 10 days. (e) After 13 days. (f) After 27 days.

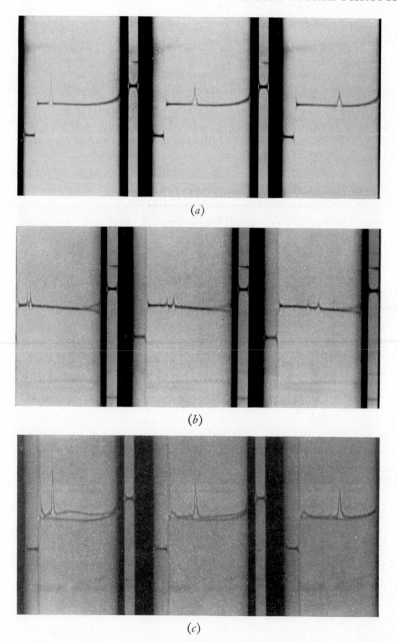

Fig. 4. Sedimentation photographs of isolated 80 S particles taken at 0, 2, and 4 minutes after UTS at 200,000g in the analytical ultracentrifuge. Particles moving from left to right. (a) 80 S particles from 24-hour stationary-phase cells observed immediately after isolation. (b) 80 S particles, isolated from 24-hour stationary cells, suspended in phosphate buffer and kept at room temperature for 2 days. (c) 80 S particles isolated from cells nitrogen-starved for 72 hours suspended in phosphate buffer and kept at room temperature for 2 days.

ments as a rapidly spreading fore peak [23] before the centrifuge is up to speed (UTS). The growing cell components disappear as starvation progresses.

The stability of microsome components isolated from log phase, stationary phase, and starving cells and kept at 4° C or at room temperature in buffered solvent was also studied. There was no detectable difference in stability between particles isolated from log phase and those isolated from stationary phase. Figure 3 shows the degradation of microsomes isolated from 48-hour stationary-phase cells and suspended in phosphate buffer at 4° C.

Since only the 80 S component is present in old stationary-phase cells and in starving cells, the stability of this component isolated from proliferating, non-proliferating, and starving cells, and dissolved in buffered solvent, was compared. Figure 4a shows the sedimentation pattern at 0, 2, and 4 minutes after UTS at 200,000g of the 80 S particles isolated from 24-hour stationary-phase cells. The sedimentation pattern of this component from 72-hour nitrogen-starved cells is similar, except for the broad, rapidly spreading, and sedimenting fore peak. As shown in figure 4b, the 80 S component isolated from log-phase and stationary-phase cells gave rise to the 60 S and 40 S component [24] when kept at room temperature for 2 days. On the other hand, the 80 S component isolated from cells nitrogen-starved for 72 hours became degraded by forming rapidly sedimenting aggregates. See figures 4c and 5.

DISCUSSION

When starved cells are given utilizable nitrogen, the growth curve shows a characteristic lag phase corresponding to the degree of starvation. During this phase the 80 S component appears to be degraded and reconstituted. As shown in figure 2, a decrease in the 80 S component is noted 1.5 hours after starved cells are given utilizable nitrogen. Two hours after inoculation, the microsomal concentration appears approximately equal to that of the inoculum cells. At 3 hours, new microsomal components appear in the cytoplasmic extract. The cells are now entering the log growth phase, during which the microsome concentration reaches a maximum. This condition is followed by a gradual quantitative change in the microsomal components as the cells pass through the stationary phase.

Chao and Schachman [8, 24] have shown that, in vitro, altering the ionic environment of the solvent will dissociate or aggregate the 80 S component. It would therefore be interesting to ascertain whether a similar mechanism is responsible for changes in the microsomal components in respiring cells.

Since the 80 S particles from only starving cells of low viability are degraded by forming rapidly sedimenting aggregates (figures 4c and 5), there appears to be a correlation between call viability and the chemical state of this particle.

Furthermore, if microsomes are involved in the synthesis of proteins and lipids [5, 15, 16], the changes observed in the microsomal components with cell growth could be a mechanism that controls their synthetic activities.

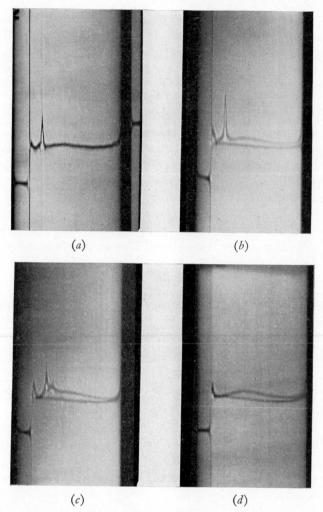

Fig. 5. Sedimentation photographs at UTS (200,000g) of 80 S particles isolated from cells nitrogen-starved for 72 hours and suspended in phosphate buffer at 4° C. (*a*) After 1 day. (*b*) After 2 days. (*c*) After 7 days. (*d*) After 11 days.

SUMMARY

Ultracentrifugal studies of yeast-cell extracts have shown a correlation between the physiological states of the cells and the stability and appearance or disappearance of microsomal particles from the cytoplasm.

ACKNOWLEDGMENT

This work was done in the Biophysics group of Donner Laboratory and was supported by contract with the Atomic Energy Commission. I wish to thank Dr. Cornelius A. Tobias for his interest in this work.

REFERENCES

1. A. Claude, *Science, 97,* 451 (1943).

2. A. Claude, *Harvey Lectures, 48,* 121 (1947–1948).

3. C. P. Barnum and R. A. Huseby, *Arch. Biochem., 19,* 17 (1948).

4. G. E. Palade and P. Siekevitz, *Federation Proc., 14,* 262 (1955).

5. J. W. Littlefield, E. B. Keller, J. Gross, and P. C. Zamecnik, *J. Biol. Chem., 217,* 111 (1955).

6. H. K. Schachman, A. B. Pardee, and R. Y. Stanier, *Arch. Biochem. Biophys., 38,* 245 (1952).

7. P. O. P. Ts'o, J. Bonner, and J. Vinograd, *J. Biophys. Biochem. Cytol., 2,* 451 (1956).

8. F. Chao and H. K. Schachman, *Arch. Biochem. Biophys., 61,* 220 (1956).

9. G. E. Palade and P. Siekevitz, *J. Biophys. Biochem. Cytol., 2,* 171 (1956).

10. G. E. Palade and P. Siekevitz, *J. Biophys. Biochem. Cytol., 2,* 671 (1956).

11. G. E. Palade, *J. Biophys. Biochem. Cytol., 1,* 59 (1955).

12. G. E. Palade and K. R. Porter, *J. Exptl. Med., 100,* 641 (1954).

13. K. R. Porter, *J. Exptl. Med., 97,* 727 (1953).

14. D. B. Slautterback, *Exptl. Cell Research, 5,* 173 (1953).

15. P. Siekevitz, *J. Biol. Chem., 195,* 549 (1952).

16. H. P. Klein, *J. Bacteriol., 73,* 530 (1957).

17. T. Hultin, *Exptl. Cell Research, 1,* 376, 599 (1950).

18. N. D. Lee, J. T. Anderson, R. Miller, and R. H. Williams, *J. Biol. Chem., 192,* 733 (1951).

19. R. M. S. Smellie, W. M. McIndoe, and J. N. Davidson, *Biochim. et Biophys. Acta, 11,* 559 (1953).

20. V. Allfrey, M. N. Daly, and A. E. Mirsky, *J. Gen. Physiol., 37,* 157 (1953).

21. P. C. Zamecnik and E. B. Keller, *J. Biol. Chem., 209,* 337 (1954).

22. R. G. Wolfe, UCRL-2553, April 1954.

23. R. G. Wolfe, *Arch. Biochem. Biophys., 63,* 100 (1956).

24. F. Chao, *Arch. Biochem. Biophys., 70,* 426 (1957).

10

Fractionation of *Escherichia coli* for Kinetic Studies

RICHARD B. ROBERTS   ROY J. BRITTEN   ELLIS T. BOLTON

*Department of Terrestrial Magnetism
Carnegie Institution of Washington*

A single cell of the bacterium *Escherichia coli* contains roughly 10,000 ribosomes (microsomal particles). If the cells are broken open and their contents are examined, the analytical centrifuge shows a series of peaks with sedimentation constants of roughly 20, 30, 40, 60, and 80 S [1–8]. The existence of these particles in such variety and in such large numbers immediately provokes a number of questions. Is the rapid growth rate of *E. coli* a consequence of the high proportion (25 per cent) of the cellular material that is organized into ribosomes? In other words, are ribosomes the sites of protein synthesis in *E. coli*? If so, what size of particle is active in protein synthesis? How are the particles themselves synthesized? Do the different sizes of particles represent different stages in the growth of a particle?

Eventually answers will be found for these questions, but not easily. It will be necessary to know the composition of the particles—the composition of the individual classes of particles, not just the composition of a pellet containing an assortment of particles plus other material. Also the kinetics of isotope incorporation will have to be studied. It will not be sufficient simply to deal with the microsomal fraction, the 100,000g pellet; rather, the individual groups of particles will have to be sorted out and measured. Suppose, for example, that one size of particle is the precursor of another. Kinetic measurements will show this clearly if the two groups can be resolved; kinetic measurements of both groups lumped together in a pellet will show nothing.

Chemical fractionation of *E. coli* gives good separation between the different classes of compounds, and it is easy to show by kinetic measurements of the incorporation of radioactive compounds that the small molecules serve as precursors of the large ones. In contrast, the simple separation into cell wall, microsome, and soluble fractions is not sufficient to reveal clearly any precursors or products among the macromolecules. A further fractionation of the microsome pellet is required.

Pellets of somewhat greater homogeneity can be obtained by choosing an appropriate centrifuging schedule. The material that sediments in 15 minutes at 100,000g is richer in the large particles than the pellet obtained by centrifuging down (2 hours at 100,000g) material which stayed in suspension during three successive 15-minute periods at 100,000g. The composition of the pellet also varies; the early pellet contains nearly twice the lipid and protein per unit of nucleic acid. This approach, however, shows no promise of giving adequate fractionation.

A somewhat better fractionation can be obtained by using the swinging bucket head for the Spinco Model L centrifuge. Microsome pellets are resuspended and layered on top of a sucrose gradient. After a period of centrifugation, layers are taken off with a pipet. This technique is adequate to show marked differences in the distributions, depending on the initial material. Figure 1 shows one curve for a resuspended pellet composed mostly of large (80 S) particles; another for the smaller particles (20 to 40 S) that result if magnesium is lacking [8]; and a third, for the nonsedimenting material. The analytical

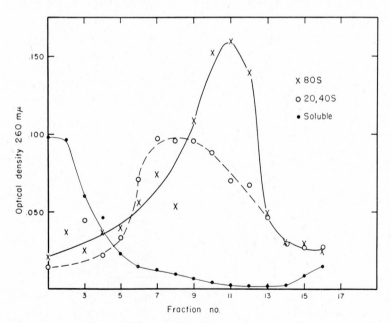

Fig. 1. Fractionation of particle preparations using the swinging bucket centrifuge. Five-tenths milliliter of suspension is placed on top of 4.5 ml sucrose gradient in the centrifuge tube. After 45 minutes at 100,000g, 0.3-ml fractions are taken off from the top with a pipet.

centrifuge shows that the bottom layers are rich in the heavy particles and lack the light particles, whereas the top layers show the opposite distribution.

Quite a different type of fractionation results from chromatography on columns of diethylaminoethyl cellulose (DEAE) [9, 10]. Extremely high resolution can be achieved giving a separation of various proteins as shown in figure 2. Nucleoprotein appears as a prominent peak in the elution diagram of the total cell juice but not in the diagram obtained with the 100,000g supernatant fluid (fig. 3). The corresponding ultraviolet diagrams show that there are in fact two nucleoprotein peaks: the first peak consists of nucleoprotein of high molecular weight which can be spun down in the centrifuge; the second

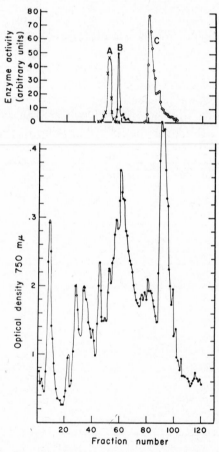

Fig. 2. Cell suspension washed and broken as described by Bolton et al. [8]; 0.5 g wet weight of cell juice adsorbed on DEAE column (1 cm² × 20 cm) and eluted with concentration gradient 0 to 0.7 M of NaCl in tris-succinate buffer plus magnesium. Lower curve, total protein indicated by Folin reaction; upper curve, assay for activity of three different enzymes. One-milliliter samples collected in fraction collector.

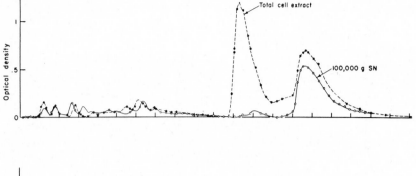

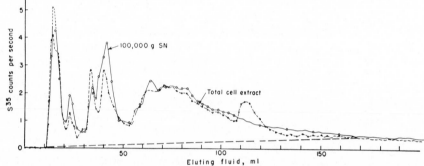

Fig. 3. Elution patterns of total cell juice and supernatant fluid of 100,000*g* 2-hour spin. Upper curve, optical density at 254, indicating nucleic acid concentration; lower curve, S^{35} radioactivity, indicating protein. Note nucleoprotein peak which is missing in 100,000*g* SN.

is partly nucleoprotein and partly due to free DNA and RNA which still remain in the 100,000*g* supernatant fluid.

The elution pattern is not sensitive to the size of the particles. The same pattern is obtained whether the microsome pellet is composed mostly of the large (80 S) particles or of the smaller 20 to 40 S particles that result from magnesium deficiency. Compare figures 4*a* and *b*.

Microsome pellets when resuspended and analyzed on the column show the nucleoprotein peak together with a quantity of other protein which depends on the method of preparation (fig. 4). A part of the contamination of the microsome pellet is due to small bits of cell wall, and another part is due to nonparticulate protein. In 2 hours at 100,000*g*, roughly 70 per cent of the β-galactosidase is sedimented. See also Dagley and Sykes [5, 11]. Accordingly the least-contaminated preparations of ribosomes are those obtained by resuspending a microsome pellet and centrifuging again in the swinging bucket head (fig. 4*c*).

Unfortunately the column cannot be used to prepare purified ribosomes because the material eluted from the column is quite different from that originally adsorbed. When the fractions containing the nucleoprotein peak are

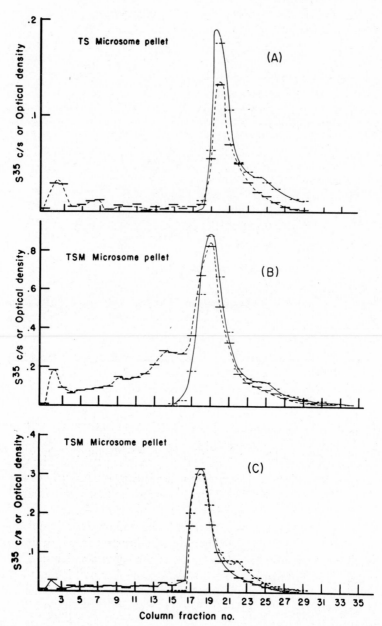

Fig. 4. Elution patterns of microsome pellets. *a,* 100,000*g* 2-hour pellet without magnesium present; *b,* same with magnesium present; *c,* microsome pellet resuspended and fractionated with swinging bucket centrifuge.

centrifuged (100,000g, 2 hours), a colorless glassy pellet is formed which contains approximately 65 per cent of the protein and nucleic acid. This pellet resuspends easily and completely. The analytical centrifuge shows that it contains peaks in the 20 to 40 S region, whereas the 80 S peak was most prominent in the original material. The ratio of nucleic acid to protein in this pellet (measured by optical density at 260 mµ and S^{35}) is twice that of the starting material, and the elution pattern obtained when the pellet is rerun on a DEAE column is very different (fig. 5).

These changes appear to be caused by the column material and not by the salt of the eluting fluid. Ribosomes exposed to molar NaCl show a reduction in size but no change in composition or elution pattern.

The fractionation and analysis procedures outlined above are beginning to yield some useful information about the composition and function of the ribosomes. The purified ribosomes are markedly different from the microsome pellet. For example, the microsome pellet contains considerable phospholipid (table 1); the ribosomes, little if any. Moreover, the nucleic acid to protein ratio is somewhat variable in the crude microsome pellet, but the purified ribosomes

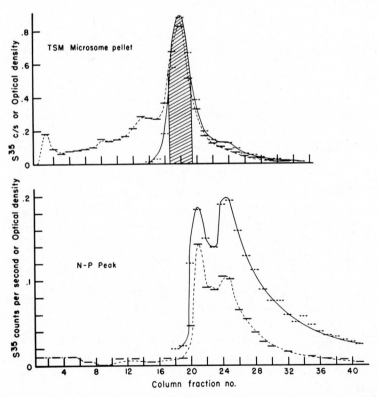

Fig. 5. Nucleoprotein peak of elution pattern spun down and rechromatographed. Note change to elution pattern like that of nucleic acid.

TABLE 1. Chemical Fractionation of *coli* Components

	Whole Cell	Cell Wall 30,000*g* pellet	Microsome 100,000*g* pellet	Soluble 100,000*g* SN
Small molecules	8	1	1	6
Lipids	7	4	3	0
RNA	15	0	13	2
DNA	3	0	0	3
Protein	67	15	13	38
Total	100	20	30	50

obtained from the swinging bucket give a constant ratio indicating two amino acids per nucleotide ($NA/P=60/40$ measured by absorption at 260 mμ and Folin [12] test for protein).

The protein of ribosomes differs from other proteins of the cell. Purified ribosomes were obtained from cells grown with C^{14} glucose as the sole carbon source. The protein, after hydrolysis and chromatography, showed an amino acid distribution in which glutamic acid, alanine, glycine, and lysine were proportionately higher than in the whole cell, whereas methionine and aspartic acid were lower. In this protein neither cysteine nor cystine seems to be present.

. The absence of cystine can best be shown by growing the cells in the presence of $S^{35}O_4$ to label cystine and methionine. After hydrolysis and chromatography the radioactivity of methionine and cystine can be measured. In the protein of the whole cell there is approximately twice as much methionine as cystine [13]. In ribosomes purified in the swinging bucket centrifuge this ratio is 10:1. In nucleoprotein eluted from the column and sedimented the ratio is greater than 100:1.

Alternatively the lack of cystine can be demonstrated without hydrolysis and chromatography. Cells containing S^{35} cystine and S^{32} methionine were grown by adding $S^{35}O_4$ and S^{32} methionine to the medium. To prevent even a slight leakage of S^{35} into methionine, a methionine-requiring mutant was used [13]. The sulfur radioactivity per unit protein of the nucleoprotein (obtained by column analysis of a microsome pellet and sedimentation of the nucleoprotein fraction of the eluate) was 50 times lower than that of the whole cell. Since the usual occurrence of cystine is only 1 per 60 residues, its occurrence in the nucleoprotein is less than 1 per 3000.

Kinetic studies of the fractions obtained from the column are also in progress. S^{35} has been used to follow incorporation into protein. Exponentially growing cells were exposed to the tracer for varying periods of time and then broken and their constituents analyzed. The specific radioactivity of the protein fractions was measured by TCA-precipitable S^{35} and Folin reaction color. When the cells are exposed to the tracer for a prolonged period (steady state) the specific radioactivity varies throughout the elution pattern by a factor of roughly 3, being lowest in the nucleoprotein fraction. These variations are simply due to variations in the sulfur content. Other cells were grown for three generations in a nonradioactive medium after exposure to the tracer. In this treatment any intermediates which have a rapid turnover should lose their radioactivity. The resulting "persistent pattern" was entirely similar to the "steady-state pattern," and no protein components could be identified as intermediates.

Finally, cells were exposed to the tracer for short periods. After a 4-minute exposure the resulting "pulse pattern" was similar to the "steady-state pattern" except that the radioactivity of the nucleoprotein peak was only one-half of that expected from the "steady-state" pattern. A similar result was obtained with cells exposed for 4 minutes to a mixture of C^{14}-labeled amino acids.

Similar experiments carried out with $P^{32}O_4$ give much more striking results. Figure 6 shows the macromolecular region of the elution patterns obtained with cells exposed to the tracer for increasing periods of time. The radioactivity appears first in a quite distinct fraction of the elution pattern, passing through at a later time to the other regions. In the steady-state and persistent patterns the phosphorus radioactivity was proportional to the optical density (at 260 mμ). Thus the DEAE column is capable of resolving the nucleic acid and nucleoprotein into fractions that seem to be precursors and products. Similar kinetic differences were also observed by Creaser, who used ECTEOLA columns [9] to analyze alcohol-extracted nucleic acid [14].

The analysis of these data runs into a number of complications. The leading peak is composed solely of RNP, but the secondary peak is an unresolved mixture of RNP, RNA, and DNA. Furthermore, the pool of low-molecular-weight precursors to RNA is large and may or may not be in equilibrium with the smaller pool of DNA precursors [14].

A rough analysis can be made on the basis of several simplifying assumptions. Assume first that the low-molecular-weight precursors of the macromole-

DE AE COLUMN ANALYSIS OF E.COLI AT EARLY TIMES AFTER ADDITION OF P³²

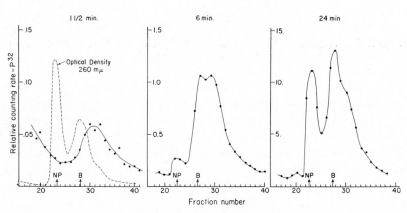

Fig. 6. Elution patterns of cell extracts after growing cells were exposed to $P^{32}O_4$ for times indicated. Only a small region of the elution pattern is shown.

cules have the average specific radioactivity of the TCA-soluble pool. Second, since the persistent and steady-state runs show all the macromolecular ultra-violet-absorbing material to be uniformly labeled, assume that it is the end product and that its specific radioactivity is that of the nucleoprotein. Analyzed on this basis the data point to an intermediate containing roughly 10 per cent of the nucleic acid.

Some other characteristics of this intermediate have been determined. Very short exposures to the tracer were used to prepare cell juices which were shown by column analysis to have most of the P^{32} in the intermediate and little in the end products. Most of the low-molecular-weight materials were removed by washing the cells with water before breaking. This material was analyzed in the swinging bucket centrifuge. The results (fig. 7) show that the TCA-precipitable radioactivity sediments at less than half the rate of the ultraviolet-absorbing material, which is mostly in 80 S ribosomes. Incubation with RNAase showed the usual rate of release of nucleotides.

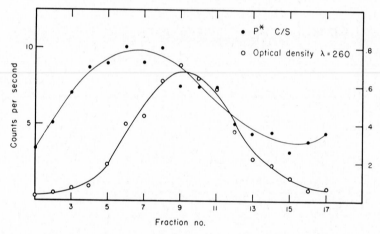

Fig. 7. Growing cells were exposed to P^{32} for 3 minutes, then broken, and the microsome pellet was analyzed in the swinging bucket centrifuge. Note that the maximum radioactivity does not correspond to the maximum of the ultraviolet absorption. Cf. figure 1.

Those findings, together with its column elution pattern, suggest that the intermediate is RNA of high molecular weight, either free or associated with less protein than the bulk of the nucleoprotein. It should be emphasized that neither lipids nor fragments of cell wall or cell membrane are eluted from the column, and it is observed that a large part of the P^{32} incorporated in short exposures is irreversibly bound to the column. An important part of the kinetics may thereby be missed.

DISCUSSION

To interpret the detailed workings of the cell in terms of its structural components, fractionation procedures are needed to separate those components. The procedures outlined above are only a step toward the needed resolution, but they have already given indications that:

1. The 80 S ribosomes are composed of nucleoprotein of approximately two amino acids per nucleotide.

2. This composition is unaltered in the smaller disintegration products resulting from magnesium deficiency.

3. Adsorption followed by elution from the DEAE column causes disintegration into smaller particles of different composition containing approximately one amino acid per nucleotide.

4. The protein of the ribosomes is a special protein or at least a special class of proteins lacking cystine and cysteine. It is therefore doubtful that any of the enzymes that have been reported in the microsome pellet are actually in the ribosome fraction.

5. The protein of the ribosomes is most certainly not precursor to the non-particulate proteins. Such a relationship is ruled out by the data on the composition and on the kinetics of formation.

6. Incorporation of amino acids, sulfur, and phosphorus into nucleoprotein of the ribosomes shows a kinetic delay which indicates that the ribosomes have a macromolecular precursor.

7. This precursor has properties suggestive of nucleic acid or nucleoprotein of a low protein content.

These findings when checked and verified will be useful in providing further conditions that must be met by any theory of protein synthesis. The low initial specific radioactivity found in the ribosome fraction differs markedly from the high initial specific radioactivity found in the deoxycholate-insoluble part of the microsome fraction of rat liver [15]. A partial explanation for the difference may be that the nucleoprotein has been stripped clean of adhering newly formed protein by the column; it is not a complete explanation, however, because the nonparticulate protein of the microsome fraction did not have a high initial specific radioactivity. More likely, the difference arises from the difference in the growth rates. If the ribosomes furnish the templates for protein synthesis, and if chains of 150 amino acid residues are produced by the ribosomes, then each of the 10,000 ribosomes of a *coli* cell must produce one polypeptide chain per 10 seconds to give the observed rate of protein synthesis. If one polypeptide chain adheres to each ribosome, after 4 minutes' exposure to the tracer only 1/24 of the newly formed polypeptide chains would be found still adhering to the particles. To show kinetic effects in protein synthesis with these rapidly growing organisms it will be necessary to use much shorter exposures to the tracer.

The synthesis of the particles themselves appears to be a distinctly different process, as it proceeds at a more leisurely rate. Even after 24 minutes there are still marked departures from the steady-state distribution. These findings are compatible with, but certainly do not prove, the idea that the smaller particles observed in the cell juice are not simply bits broken off during disruption of the cell, but that they have biological significance and that they may represent stages in the growth cycle of the particles.

REFERENCES

1. S. E. Luria, M. Delbruck, and T. Anderson, *J. Bacteriol., 46,* 57 (1943).

2. H. K. Schachman, A. B. Pardee, and R. Y. Stanier, *Arch. Biochem. Biophys., 38,* 245 (1952).

3. A. Siegel, S. J. Singer, and S. G. Wildman, *Arch. Biochem. Biophys., 41,* 278 (1952).

4. D. Billen and E. Volkin, *J. Bacteriol., 67,* 191 (1954).

5. S. Dagley and J. Sykes, *Arch. Biochem. Biophys., 63,* 338 (1956).

6. H. E. Wade and D. M. Morgan, *Biochem. J., 65,* 321 (1957).

7. A. B. Pardee, K. Paigen, and L. S. Prestidge, *Biochim. et Biophys. Acta, 23,* 162 (1957).

8. E. T. Bolton, B. H. Hoyer, and D. B. Ritter, paper 3 of this volume.

9. E. A. Peterson and H. A. Sober, *J. Am. Chem. Soc., 78,* 751 (1956).

10. Report of the Biophysics Section, Department of Terrestrial Magnetism, *Carnegie Inst. Wash. Year Book 56,* p. 118, Washington, D. C., 1957.

11. S. Dagley, paper 7 of this volume.

12. O. H. Lowry, N. J. Rosebrough, A. Furr, A. Lewis, and R. J. Randall, *J. Biol. Chem., 193,* 265 (1951).

13. R. B. Roberts, P. H. Abelson, D. B. Cowie, E. T. Bolton, and R. J. Britten, *Studies of Biosynthesis in Escherichia coli,* Carnegie Inst. Wash. Publ. 607, Washington, D. C., 1955.

14. Report of the Biophysics Section, Department of Terrestrial Magnetism, *Carnegie Inst. Wash. Year Book 55,* p. 110, Washington, D. C., 1956.

15. W. Littlefield, E. B. Keller, J. Gross, and P. C. Zamecnik, *J. Biol. Chem., 217,* 111 (1955). See also J. Brachet, *Biochemical Cytology,* pp. 41–47, 240–286, 296–355, Academic Press, New York, 1957.

11

Microsomal Structure and Hemoglobin Synthesis in the Rabbit Reticulocyte

HOWARD M. DINTZIS   HENRY BORSOOK   JEROME VINOGRAD

Gates and Crellin Laboratories of Chemistry
and Kerckhoff Laboratories of Biology
California Institute of Technology

A great deal of evidence has now accumulated which suggests very strongly that microsomal particles are somehow connected with the process of protein synthesis [1, 2, 3]. Because of their high content of ribonucleic acid which might act as a coding template, it has become fashionable to postulate that these particles are the actual sites of protein assembly from activated single amino acids. To date, however, no evidence has been put forth which could be called direct proof that such is indeed the case.

Nevertheless, the hypothesis is so attractive that it seems worth while to proceed on the assumption that it is true and to investigate the detailed structure of microsomal particles and the relation of this structure to the protein which the particles are supposedly synthesizing. Such a study would have as its object an understanding of the molecular nature of the microsomal particle, the molecular structure of the growing peptide chains of the protein being synthesized, and, if possible, the interrelation between the two.

To best carry out such a study, one would like to find a system consisting of free floating cells of a single type, actively engaged in the synthesis of predominantly a single type of protein molecule. Fortunately these desirable properties are exhibited by mammalian reticulocytes. Such cells can be made in quantity if rabbits are made anemic by daily injections of phenylhydrazine. After a week of such injections, reticulocytes (immature red cells) account for 80 to 90 per cent of the red cells present in the blood. These cells are actively producing hemoglobin and will continue to do so for many hours if suspended in the proper incubation medium [4, 5]. During such incubation, hemoglobin accounts for over 90 per cent of the protein produced.

The microsomal fraction of rabbit reticulocytes has been shown to be very active in incorporating radioactive amino acids [6]. The following work represents a beginning step toward an understanding of the relationship between microsomal structure and hemoglobin synthesis in the sense described above.

SOME PROPERTIES OF MICROSOMAL PARTICLES

Preliminary experiments on isolation of the microsomal fraction showed that the predominant component had a sedimentation coefficient of about 80 S. Variations in the method of breaking the cells and in the buffer used for isolating the microsomal particles were explored before the following standard procedure was developed. The reticulocytes were frozen, thawed, and mixed with 3 volumes of cold buffer containing 0.14 M KCl, 0.001 M $MgCl_2$, and 0.01 M trischloride, pH 7.2. Cell walls and debris were spun out at low speed. Microsomes were then pelleted at 100,000g for 3 hours. The red pellet thus obtained was then twice redissolved and respun in 100 volumes of buffer, giving a light amber-colored pellet after the third centrifugation.

Microsomal particles prepared in this way were found to give three components in the ultracentrifuge: 82 per cent of 78 S, 9 per cent of 120 S, and 9 per cent of 50 to 60 S. On electrophoresis in the same buffer the preparation showed a negative charge, and migrated with only slight skewing in the descending limb and a splitting into two components in the ascending limb.

The intrinsic viscosity was found to be 0.08 dl/g in the buffer, and the partial specific volume was found to be 0.63 ml/g.

From these numbers it may be calculated that, if the particles are spherical, the hydration is 2.6 g of water per gram of anhydrous particle, a very high value indeed. Taking as a model a highly hydrated sphere, one calculates a frictional coefficient of 1.72 and a molecular weight of 4.1×10^6.

That such a model cannot be very far wrong was indicated by light-scattering measurements on the same preparations. These showed a molecular weight of 4×10^6 and a measured dissymmetry of 1.08 ($45°/135°$) with light of the mercury blue line. Since a dissymmetry of 1.06 is to be expected for a hydrated sphere of this molecular weight (diameter, 340 A), the axial ratio cannot be far from unity, and shapes such as rods and random coils are definitely excluded.

The protein/RNA ratio for these particles was found to be almost unity on a weight basis. No lipid could be extracted. If the RNA from these particles is banded in an equilibrium density gradient [7] in cesium formate, the molecular weight of the RNA is found to be approximately 500,000. This is consistent with a small integral number of RNA molecules per microsomal particle. If the above molecular weights are accepted, this integral number is 4.

BIOLOGICAL ACTIVITY OF MICROSOMAL PARTICLES

In the following experiments rabbit reticulocytes were centrifuged several times in buffer, suspended at 37° in a medium containing amino acids, iron, and other materials necessary to ensure optimal hemoglobin syntheses. A given C^{14} labeled amino acid was added, and the living cells were incubated for a definite time period; then several volumes of ice-cold saline were added and the cells centrifuged several times from cold saline to remove extracellular label. The cells were then frozen, and microsomes were prepared as described above.

When the cells were incubated for various time intervals with carboxyl C^{14} labeled leucine (15,500 cpm/mg) the resultant specific activities of protein in microsomes and in hemoglobin were as shown in table 1.

It would appear that a steady-state concentration of labeled amino acids in the microsomes is reached within approximately 10 minutes or less.

TABLE 1

Incubation Time, min.	Specific Activity, cpm/mg protein		Rate of Activity Increase in Hemoglobin, cpm/mg/min
	Microsomes	Hemoglobin	
0	0.02	0.01	. . .
1	0.6	0.11	0.11
5	1.1	1.1	0.22
15	1.7	4.3	0.29
60	1.8	12.3	0.21
240	3.1	34.9	0.15

The labeled amino acid in the purified microsomes is present in some tightly bound form, as shown by the facts that (1) it is not removed at all by dissolving the microsomes in buffer saturated with nonlabeled leucine and (2) little, if any, count is removed by extraction with trichloroacetic acid.

However, the label is rapidly turned over in the living cell, as shown by the fact that if cells are labeled for 15 minutes in medium containing radioleucine, and then placed in medium containing nonlabeled leucine for 15 minutes, 90 per cent of the label is removed from the microsomes. This shows that most of the label present in the microsomal particle is in a dynamic state, and is not a permanent part of the microsome structure.

In order to obtain information concerning the amino acid composition of the transient material in the microsome, experiments were conducted using various labeled amino acids in the incubation medium. Radioleucine was always run as a control, and the molar ratios of other amino acids to leucine were determined in the hemoglobin and microsomes after 15 minutes of incubation. The results are summarized in table 2, where the labeled amino acid ratios are compared with the total amino acid ratios determined by microbiological assay. It can be seen that the leucine-histidine ratio of transient material in the microsome is compatible with the supposition that this material is hemoglobin protein and not microsome structural protein. The leucine-phenylalanine ratio is not very informative, and the measured leucine-arginine ratio, which lies almost exactly half way between microsomal protein and hemoglobin, is very ambiguous. These results are compatible with the assumption that the transient material in the microsome is largely pre-hemoglobin. More evidence is needed to confirm this assumption, however.

TABLE 2. Molar Ratios of Leucine to Various Amino Acids

	Microsomes		Hemoglobin	
	Total Composition	Label	Total Composition	Label
Histidine	3.7	2.2	1.8	1.9
Phenylalanine	2.5	2.1	2.3	2.0
Arginine	1.0	3.2	5.7	7.5

Boiling microsomes with 66 per cent ethanol extracted about 25 per cent of the radioactive material, whose free amino nitrogen increased greatly on refluxing with 6 N HCl, suggesting that this material is peptide in nature. The specific activity of the material was 5 to 10 times that of the unextracted microsomal protein. Both the extractable and nonextractable radioactive materials were transient; i.e., the counts were removed on incubating cells in nonlabeled amino acid for 15 minutes.

One would like to conclude from the above extraction data that the extracted material is richer than the whole microsome in growing peptide chains of short length, whereas the unextractable material represents growing peptide chains which are too long to dissolve in 66 per cent ethanol. The short chains would presumably represent the earliest stages of hemoglobin formation in the microsome. Further purification and characterization are necessary to prove this point.

SOME NUMEROLOGY AND CONCLUSIONS

The above data lead to some interesting results if the following assumptions (or approximations) are made: (1) hemoglobin is the only protein being made in rabbit reticulocytes; (2) all microsomal particles are equally active in synthesizing hemoglobin; (3) all the transient label in the microsome is pre-hemoglobin. The steady-state label level of the microsomal particle, the specific activity of leucine used, together with the facts that 12 per cent of the protein is leucine and one-half of the microsome is protein, lead to the conclusion that 0.05 per cent of the mass of the microsomal particle is pre-hemoglobin, i.e., growing peptide chain. Since the molecular weight of the microsomal particle is 4,000,000 as shown above, this means that the average weight of growing chain per particle is 2000. In a random population of growing chains the average weight might be expected to be about one-half of the finished chain weight. If all the growing chain per particle is in one piece, this leads to a value of 4000 for the finished weight of polypeptide chain made per microsomal particle, a value reasonably close to the weight of one-fourth of a hemoglobin molecule, i.e., one polypeptide chain. If assumption 2 above is incorrect, and only a fraction of the microsomal particles is functional, the agreement is even better. From the rate of incorporation of label into finished hemoglobin molecules and the concentrations in the living cells of hemoglobin (15 per cent) and microsomes (0.5 per cent), one may calculate that to account for the production of new hemoglobin each microsomal particle must make one-quarter of a hemoglobin in 1.5 minutes.

SUMMARY

The above data lead to the picture of a microsomal particle as an almost spherical sponge-like structure of anhydrous molecular weight 4,000,000 and diameter 340 A. One-half of the mass is represented by ribonucleic acid which appears to be present as four strands of molecular weight 500,000. The half of the microsomal particle which is protein appears to be almost entirely (99.9 per cent) structural in nature; i.e., it is *not* transient protein precursor.

Woven into this sponge-like structure in some way is a very small amount (0.05 per cent by weight) of transient protein precursor. Taken together with the observed rate of hemoglobin production, this amount of precursor is compatible with the conclusion that one microsomal particle makes one polypeptide chain of hemoglobin in approximately 1 minute.

Contribution No. 2338

REFERENCES

1. H. Borsook, C. L. Deasy, A. J. Haagen-Smit, G. Keighley, and P. H. Lowy, *J. Biol. Chem., 187,* 839 (1950).

2. J. W. Littlefield, E. B. Keller, J. Gross, and P. C. Zamecnik, *J. Biol. Chem., 217,* 111 (1955).

3. J. W. Littlefield and E. B. Keller, *J. Biol. Chem., 224,* 13 (1957).

4. J. Kruh and H. Borsook, *J. Biol. Chem., 220,* 905 (1956).

5. H. Borsook, E. H. Fischer, and G. Keighley, *J. Biol. Chem., 229,* 1059 (1957).

6. M. Rabinovitz and M. E. Olson, *Exptl. Cell Research, 10,* 747 (1956).

7. M. Meselson, F. W. Stahl, and J. Vinograd, *Proc. Natl. Acad. Sci. U. S., 43,* 581 (1957).

12

Effects of p-Fluorophenylalanine on the Growth and Physiology of Yeast[1]

G. N. COHEN   H. O. HALVORSON

Department of Bacteriology, University of Wisconsin

S. SPIEGELMAN

Department of Bacteriology, University of Illinois

Halvorson and Spiegelman [1] examined a series of amino acid analogs for their ability to inhibit growth of yeast, to deplete the "free amino acid pool," and to synthesize protein. When exponentially growing yeast is washed and resuspended in a nitrogen-free buffer in the presence of glucose, the free amino acids are rapidly incorporated into proteins, thus depleting the amino acid pool. In the presence of high concentrations of p-fluorophenylalanine (10^{-2} M to 2×10^{-2} M), this depletion is severely inhibited, as shown by chromatographic study of the pool components or by analysis of the glutamic acid content of the pool. This inhibition was interpreted as follows: The presence of an amino acid analog prevents the incorporation not only of its natural homolog but of all the other amino acids as well.

On the other hand, Munier and Cohen [2] found that p-fluorophenylalanine, when added to an exponentially growing culture of *Escherichia coli*, caused a linear growth. During that period the differential rate of incorporation of valine or S^{35}

$$(\Delta \text{valine or } \Delta S^{35})/\Delta \text{mass}$$

was the same as in a control culture, although incorporation was somewhat slower than during exponential growth. Radioactive amino acids were formed

[1] This investigation was aided by a grant (G-4258) from the Division of Biological and Medical Sciences of the National Science Foundation.

from radioactive glucose and incorporated in the presence of the analog during the linear growth. In addition, *p*-fluorophenylalanine was incorporated (Munier and Cohen [2], [3]) to a great extent (up to 200 mµmoles/g dry weight). Induced β-galactosidase was synthesized at the same differential rate as in a control culture without analog. Because of the contradictory results of these two studies, it was decided to re-examine the effects of *p*-fluorophenylalanine on yeast.

MATERIALS AND METHODS

Saccharomyces italicus Y1225 was used in these experiments. The cultures were grown in synthetic medium (Halvorson and Spiegelman [1]) in Erlenmeyer flasks which were shaken at 30° C. During the exponential phase of growth, the protein content per cell was found to be proportional to the optical density. Therefore, for reasons of convenience, growth was followed by measurements of the optical density in a Beckman DU Spectrophotometer at 600 mµ. Under these conditions 1.00 O D$=772$ µg dry wt./ml.

Viable counts were determined by plating appropriate dilutions on dextrose broth agar medium.

The cells were centrifuged, washed, and fractionated for isotope distribution as previously described (Halvorson [4]). The components of the protein hydrolysates were identified by radioautography. For radioactivity measurements, aliquots were evaporated to dryness on stainless-steel planchets and counted in a gas flow counter, and the radioactivities were corrected to infinite thinness.

The photomicrographs were taken on a 35-mm microfile film with a 100 apochromatic objective, N. A.$=1.30$. Magnification on the film was 1250×. 3-C^{14}-DL-phenylalanine (Phe) (2.1 mc/mmole), 4-4'-C^{14}-DL-valine (1.33 mc/mmole), and 3-C^{14}-DL-p-fluorophenylalanine (*p*-FPhe) (2.35mc/mmole) were obtained from the Commissariat à l'Énergie Atomique, France. Uniformly labeled glucose (2.4 mc/mmole) was obtained from the Fisher Scientific Company, and carrier-free S^{35} sulfate from the Oak Ridge National Laboratory.

RESULTS

Effects of p-Fluorophenylalanine and β-2 Thienylalanine on the Growth of Yeast. Figure 1 shows that, upon addition of 10^{-2} M *p*-FPhe or β-2 thienylalanine (Thiala) to an exponentially growing culture of yeast, the mass increases at a rate which is linear with time, as previously observed with *E. coli*. In this particular experiment, from the time of addition to the termination of growth, the mass increased 4 times in the presence of *p*-FPhe and 2.7 times in the presence of Thiala. Under these conditions, although no component of the medium was limiting for growth, there was no increase in viable count in the presence of the antagonists. The increase in optical density in the presence of *p*-FPhe (4 times) can be attributed to an increase in cell size (fig. 2). Assuming that yeast cells are ellipsoids of revolution, the average cell volume increased approximately 3.6 times in the presence of *p*-FPhe.

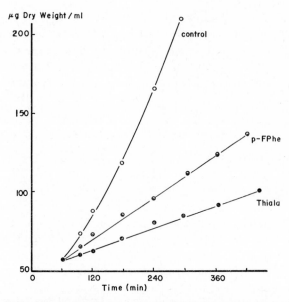

Fig. 1.   Effects of *p*-fluorophenylalanine and β-2-thienylalanine on the growth of yeast.

Synthesis of Cell Material during Linear Growth. Washed cells from an exponentially growing culture were placed in two flasks, one containing C^{14} glucose, and the other containing C^{14} glucose and *p*-FPhe (10^{-2} M final concentration).

Optical density was followed throughout the experiment, and 10-ml samples taken at intervals were placed in precooled centrifuge tubes (0° C). The cells in the control culture were allowed to increase 2.6 times, and those in the linear culture 1.9 times. The samples were fractionated (Halvorson [4]), and the radioactivity of the hot-TCA-soluble fraction (containing the nucleic acids) and of the protein fraction (hot-TCA-insoluble) was determined. The differential rates of synthesis of total hot-TCA-soluble material and of total protein were then plotted. The differential rate of synthesis of a component X is expressed by $\Delta X/\Delta M$, M being the increase in mass during the time necessary

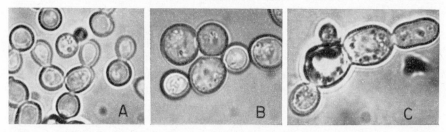

Fig. 2.   Effect of *p*-fluorophenylalanine on the size of yeast cells. Pictures taken initially (*A*), after an optical density increase of 2.7 times (*B*), and 5.4 times (*C*).

to obtain the increase ΔX; this expression is independent of the rate of growth. Figures 3 and 4 show that the differential rates of synthesis of hot-TCA-soluble material and of protein are the same in the presence and absence of p-FPhe.

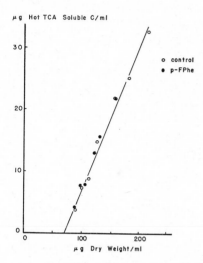

Fig. 3. Differential rate of synthesis of total hot-TCA-soluble material in the presence or absence of p-fluorophenylalanine. See text for details.

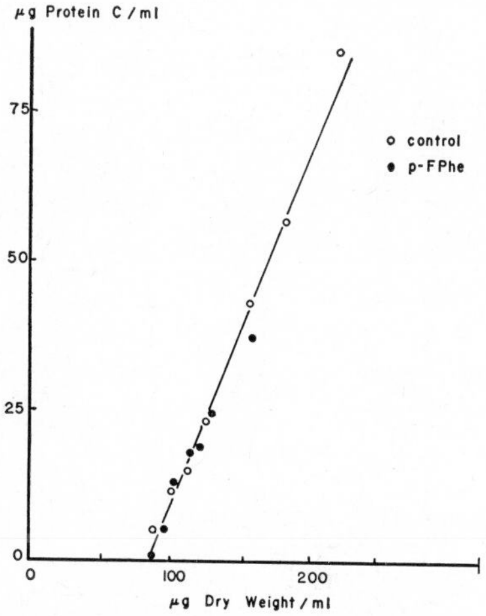

Fig. 4. Differential rate of synthesis of proteins in the presence or absence of p-fluorophenylalanine. See text for details.

Incorporation of C^{14}-p-Fluorophenylalanine in Exponentially Growing Yeast. Radioactive p-FPhe was added to two exponentially growing cultures at final concentrations of 3.87×10^{-4} M and 1.04×10^{-3} M, and the cultures were allowed to grow linearly (300 minutes) until their mass increased by 3.6 times. Samples were taken at given intervals, and the radioactivity of the protein fraction was determined. The differential rate of incorporation of p-FPhe was calculated, and from the slopes of the straight lines obtained (fig. 5) the content of p-FPhe in the proteins was found. As in *E. coli*, increasing the external concentrations of p-FPhe increases the analog content of the proteins. The incorporation is far from negligible, reaching 12 per cent of the normal phenylalanine content for a concentration of the analog of 1.03×10^{-3} M (31.2 μmoles p-FPhe/g dry wt.). Munier (personal communication) and Kerridge (quoted in Gale and McQuillen [5]) have also shown that p-FPhe is incorporated into yeast proteins. The relative amount of phenylalanine in yeast was determined from its differential rate of incorporation. In two experiments, where the C^{14} phenylalanine concentration was 3.12×10^{-5} M and 6.25×10^{-5} M respectively, identical differential rates of incorporation were observed.

In all experiments, radioautograms of the acid hydrolysates of the protein fractions were made. Both for cells grown on C^{14}-Phe and for those grown on C^{14}-p-FPhe, the radioactivity of the protein hydrolysates was identified exclusively with the added isotope.

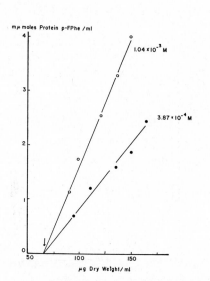

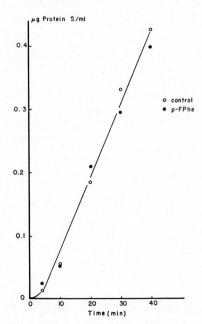

Fig. 5. Differential rate of incorporation of *p*-fluorophenylalanine. See text for details.

Fig. 6. Effect of *p*-fluorophenylalanine on S³⁵ sulfate incorporation into proteins of resting yeast cells. See text for details.

Incorporation of p-Fluorophenylalanine under "Resting" Conditions. Since the experiments of Halvorson and Spiegelman [1] were conducted with "resting" cells, it was interesting to know whether incorporation of *p*-FPhe occurred also under these conditions. Exponentially growing yeast was washed twice with buffer and resuspended in phosphate-succinate buffer, *p*H 4.7, with glucose as energy source, but without an exogenous nitrogen source. The suspension was divided in two flasks to which C¹⁴ Phe and C¹⁴ *p*-FPhe were respectively added (final concentration: 6.25×10^{-3} *M*). In both flasks the incorporation of radioisotope was linear with time and ceased after 50 minutes' incubation. At this time, 31.8 mμmoles of Phe had been incorporated, whereas 19.4 mμmoles of *p*-FPhe had been incorporated in the proteins per milliliter of culture. Thus, the analog was incorporated at 61 per cent the extent of Phe incorporation.

Incorporation of Sulfur from Radiosulfate into Yeast Proteins under "Resting" Conditions. An exponential culture from synthetic medium was centrifuged, washed, resuspended in nitrogen-free medium, and divided in two flasks containing S³⁵ with and without 0.01 *M p*-FPhe. The incorporation of S³⁵ into proteins was linear with time over 40 minutes with identical slopes of incorporation in the two flasks (fig. 6).

Incorporation of Radiovaline under "Resting" Conditions in Presence or Absence of p-FPhe. Yeast was grown in broth, centrifuged while in the exponential phase, washed twice, and resuspended in phosphate-succinate buffer with glucose but without an exogenous source of nitrogen. Radioactive valine was added at 0 time, and the suspension was shaken for 8 minutes at 30° C. The suspension was then centrifuged, washed twice in the cold, and divided into two flasks in the same medium without valine, and with and without 10^{-2} M p-FPhe. Valine incorporation proceeded at the same rate in the two flasks (fig. 7); as shown previously (Halvorson and Cohen [6]), the valine pool size is sufficient under these conditions for an unchanged rate of valine incorporation. These experiments show that, under growing or "resting" conditions, p-FPhe does not inhibit protein synthesis. It was then interesting to find out why, under the conditions of Halvorson and Spiegelman [1], the pools were not depleted in the presence of p-FPhe.

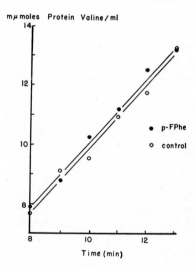

Fig. 7. Valine incorporation into the proteins of resting yeast cells. See text for details.

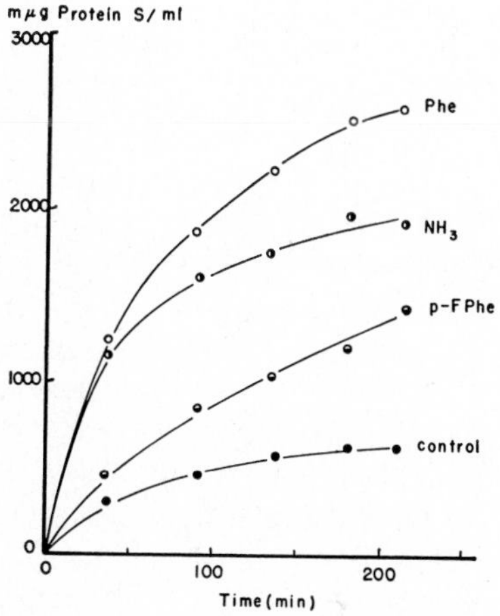

Fig. 8. Effect of exogenous nitrogen on the incorporation of S^{35} into proteins in nitrogen-starved cells. See text for details.

The Effect of Nitrogenous Compounds on the Incorporation of Sulfur into Proteins in Nitrogen-Starved Cells. A culture growing exponentially in broth was centrifuged, resuspended with glucose in a phosphate-succinate buffer, and then shaken for 18 hours (original dry weight: 1.55 mg/ml). These starved cells were then washed and resuspended in nitrogen-free, phosphate-succinate buffer with glucose and S^{35} sulfate with or without 10^{-2} M NH_4Cl, 10^{-2} M Phe, or 10^{-2} M p-FPhe. The curves of figure 8 show that p-FPhe and Phe can act as nitrogen sources for S incorporation, probably providing $-NH_2$ groups through transamination to carbon acceptors.

Effect of p-Fluorophenylalanine on Protein Degradation. In the absence of an exogenous source of nitrogen and energy, the degradation of cellular proteins leads to elevated pool levels (Halvorson [7]). Since high amino acid pool levels are observed in the presence of p-FPhe (Halvorson and Spiegelman [1]), a direct test of its effect on the rate of protein degradation was undertaken.

Cells were grown overnight in synthetic medium in the presence of radioactive valine or Phe. They were then centrifuged, washed, resuspended in fresh synthetic medium containing glucose, and shaken for 210 minutes in order to diminish any pool radioactivity that might have been present. The cells were again centrifuged, washed twice, and resuspended to a density of 3 mg dry wt./ml in two flasks containing buffer with or without p-FPhe 10^{-2} M. Protein degradation was followed by the appearance of radioactivity in the soluble pool (cold-TCA-soluble radioactivity). The results in table 1 show elevated pool levels in the presence of p-FPhe. Since the previous experiments show that p-FPhe does not inhibit the amino acid incorporation observed in the presence of an exogenous source of energy, these results indicate that the antagonist accelerates the rate of protein degradation.

TABLE 1.   Effect of p-Fluorophenylalanine on Protein Breakdown

Growth Supplement	Incubation time,* min	Radioactivity Released †	
		Control	p-FPhe
C14 valine ‡	60	0	90
	120	40	210
	180	145	380
	240	270	870
C14 phenylalanine §	60	54	463
	120	171	870
	180	378	1460
	240	613	2310

 * Incubated aerobically in phosphate buffer, pH 4.5, at 30° C with or without 0.01 M p-FPhe.
 † Increase in cpm of cold-TCA-soluble fraction/ml incubation mixture.
 ‡ 19,860 cpm protein/ml incubation mixture.
 § 81,320 cpm protein/ml incubation mixture.

DISCUSSION

A reanalysis of the effects of p-FPhe on the growth of yeast shows a strong parallelism with its effects on $E.$ $coli$. A linear rather than exponential rate of growth is seen in the absence of cell division and without decreasing the differential rates of synthesis of protein and hot-TCA-soluble material or total carbon incorporation. Furthermore, in resting yeast cells, the incorporation of endogenous amino acids is not influenced by the presence of p-FPhe. The previously observed inhibition of α-glucosidase synthesis by p-FPhe (Halvorson and Spiegelman [1]) may therefore represent another example of inactive enzyme synthesis (Cohen and Munier [8]). In contrast to the results found with $E.$ $coli$, however, p-FPhe is capable of completely suppressing α-glucosidase induction in resting yeast cells only when added simultaneously with the inducer (Halvorson and Jackson [9]). When p-FPhe was added at various times after the inducer, induced synthesis became more and more refractory to the inhibitor.

One feature of the effect of p-FPhe on resting yeast cells requires special attention. Previous studies showed that, in the presence of p-FPhe, the contents of the free amino acid pool remained essentially the same as in unstarved cells (Halvorson and Spiegelman [1]). On the basis of the present experiments, the nondisappearance of the pool in the presence of p-FPhe can be attributed to: (1) partial replenishment of the free amino acid pool from the nitrogen of p-FPhe, and (2) an increased rate of protein degradation in the presence of p-FPhe.

The reversal of p-FPhe inhibition by Phe can be related not only to a competition between these two amino acids for an accumulating system (Halvorson and Cohen [6]) but also to its incorporation into proteins. Halvorson and Spiegelman [1] had derived from their experiments with p-FPhe the conclusion that there were no intermediate precursors of induced maltozymase in yeast. Although amino acid antagonists may prove valuable for studies on protein synthesis, it would seem on the basis of these and other experiments (Cohen and Munier [8]) that conclusions derived from their use as a tool in the study of intermediates in protein synthesis are unwarranted. The *de novo* nature of induced enzyme synthesis has been established on other grounds, however (Hogness, Cohn, and Monod [10]; Rotman and Spiegelman [11]).

ACKNOWLEDGMENTS

We wish to express our appreciation to Dr. R. Munier for advice and assistance in the early phases of these experiments and to Dr. Pichat of the Commissariat à l'Énergie Atomique, France, for the synthesis of $3\text{-}C^{14}\text{-}DL\text{-}p\text{-}$fluorophenylalanine.

SUMMARY

The addition of 0.01 M p-fluorophenylalanine to a growing culture of *Saccharomyces italicus* Y1225 results in (1) an incorporation of the analog into cellular proteins, (2) a linear rather than an exponential rate of growth as a function of time, and (3) an inhibition of cell division. The antagonist does not influence the differential rates of synthesis of protein and hot-TCA-soluble material.

Under "resting conditions," p-fluorophenylalanine does not inhibit either protein synthesis or the utilization of the free amino acid pool. Elevated pools in the presence of the antagonist were attributed to pool replenishment from the nitrogen of antagonist and to an increased rate of protein degradation.

REFERENCES

1. H. O. Halvorson and S. Spiegelman, The inhibition of enzyme formation by amino acid analogues, *J. Bacteriol., 64,* 207 (1952).

2. R. L. Munier and G. N. Cohen,

Incorporation d'analogues structuraux d'amino acides dans les protéines bactériennes, *Biochim. et Biophys. Acta, 21,* 592–593 (1956).

3. R. L. Munier and G. N. Cohen,

Incorporation d'analogues structuraux d'amino acides dans les protéines *d'Escherichia coli, Ann. inst. Pasteur,* in press.

4. H. O. Halvorson, Studies on protein and nucleic acid turnover in growing cultures of yeast, *Biochim. et Biophys. Acta, 27,* 267 (1958).

5. E. F. Gale and K. McQuillen, Nitrogen metabolism, *Ann. Rev. Microbiol., 11,* 283 (1957).

6. H. O. Halvorson and G. N. Cohen, Incorporation comparée des amino acides endogènes et exogènes dans les protéines de la levure, *Ann. inst. Pasteur,* in press.

7. H. O. Halvorson, Intracellular protein and nucleic acid turnover in resting yeast cells, *Biochim. et Biophys. Acta, 27,* 255 (1958).

8. G. N. Cohen and R. L. Munier, Effect des analogues structuraux d'amino acides sur la croissance, la synthèse de protéines et la synthèse d'enzymes, chez *Escherichia coli, Ann. inst. Pasteur,* in press.

9. H. O. Halvorson and L. Jackson, The relation of ribose nucleic acid to the early stages of induced enzyme synthesis in yeast, *J. Gen. Microbiol., 14,* 26 (1956).

10. D. Hogness, M. Cohn, and J. Monod, Induced synthesis of beta-galactosidase in *E. coli, Biochim. et Biophys. Acta, 16,* 99 (1955).

11. B. Rotman and S. Spiegelman, On the origin of the carbon in the induced synthesis of beta-galactosidase in *Escherichia coli, J. Bacteriol., 68,* 419 (1954).

13

Enzymatic and Nonenzymatic Synthesis in Adenyl Tryptophan[1]

MARVIN KARASEK
P. R. KRISHNASWAMY

PAUL CASTELFRANCO [2]
ALTON MEISTER

Department of Biochemistry, Tufts University School of Medicine

Acyl adenylates have been postulated as intermediates in the activation of acetate [1] and of fatty acids [2, 3], as well as in the synthesis of phenylacetyl-glutamine and hippurate [4]. Thus, the activation of acetate and of phenylacetate may be represented as follows: [3]

$$\text{Acetate} + \text{ATP} \rightleftarrows \text{Acetyl-AMP} + \text{PP}$$
$$\text{Phenylacetate} + \text{ATP} \rightleftarrows \text{Phenylacetyl-AMP} + \text{PP}$$

The activation of amino acids, which has been observed with several enzyme preparations, appears to involve an analogous reaction [5, 6, 7, 8]:

$$\text{Amino acid} + \text{ATP} \rightleftarrows \text{Aminoacyl-AMP} + \text{PP}$$

This reaction has been followed by observing the formation of amino acid hydroxamate when enzyme preparations are incubated with amino acid, magnesium ions, adenosine triphosphate, and high concentrations of hydroxylamine. The reaction has also been observed by determining the rate of exchange of radioactive inorganic pyrophosphate with adenosine triphosphate in the presence of magnesium ions, amino acid, and enzyme.

That the intermediate formed in the activation of amino acids is an aminoacyl adenylate of the type (fig. 1) postulated to occur in other systems [1–4] is suggested by several observations. For example, synthetic acyl adenylates are

[1] Supported in part by research grants from the National Science Foundation and the National Institutes of Health, Public Health Service.
[2] Postdoctorate fellow of the National Heart Institute, Public Health Service.
[3] Abbreviations: adenosine triphosphate, ATP; adenylic acid, AMP; pyrophosphate, PP.

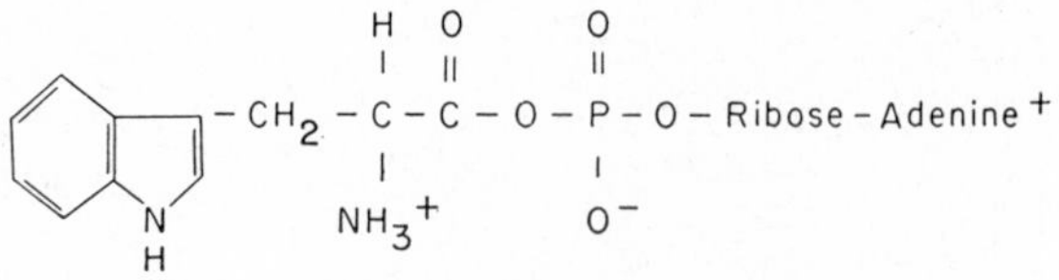

Fig. 1. Tryptophanyl adenylate.

known to react promptly with hydroxylamine to yield the corresponding hydroxamates [1–4]. Furthermore, it has been reported that synthetic leucyl
adenylate formed adenosine triphosphate when incubated with inorganic pyrophosphate and an activating enzyme purified from *Escherichia coli* [8]; a similar experiment has been carried out with methionyl adenylate and an activating enzyme isolated from yeast [6]. An additional piece of evidence consistent
with the formation of an anhydride linkage between the phosphoric acid
group of adenylic acid and the carboxyl group of amino acids has been obtained in experiments with amino acids labeled with O^{18}; transfer of O^{18} from
the carboxyl group of the amino acid to adenylic acid was associated with
enzymatic activation. The pyrophosphate formed did not contain appreciable
quantities of O^{18} [9].

The available data are consistent with the hypothesis that aminoacyl adenylates are intermediates in the amino acid activation reaction, but the formation
of such anhydrides has not yet been shown. Although there is as yet no experimental demonstration of the net synthesis of acyl adenylates in acetate or fatty
acid oxidation, the respective enzyme systems are apparently able to utilize
added synthetic acyl adenylate derivatives [1–3]. Previous inability to detect
the formation of such intermediate anhydrides may be related to the instability
of the anhydrides and perhaps also to the high affinity of the enzyme for the
anhydride; accordingly the actual intermediate in these activation reactions
may be enzyme-bound acyl adenylate.

We have attempted to obtain evidence for the net synthesis of tryptophanyl
adenylate by the tryptophan-activating enzyme of beef pancreas [7]. In these
studies, we have used aminoacyl adenylates prepared as described in the following paper by Castelfranco et al. [10]. Although tryptophanyl adenylate is
hydrolyzed rapidly at pH 7.2 and 37° C, we have found that only about 10 per
cent of the anhydride is hydrolyzed in 2 hours at pH 4.5 and 0°. Paper
ionophoresis at pH 4.5 in 0.05 M ammonium formate buffer at 0° indicated
that tryptophanyl adenylate was positively charged and moved with a greater
mobility than tryptophan itself (fig. 2). The positively charged band quenched
the fluorescence of the paper under ultraviolet light and gave the ninhydrin
color reaction. Elution of this material from the paper strip yielded an alkali-
labile compound which formed a hydroxamic acid promptly on treatment with
hydroxylamine. The hydroxamate was identified as tryptophan hydroxamate
by paper chromatography in several solvent systems. Incubation of the eluted
compound with the tryptophan-activating enzyme, magnesium chloride, inor-

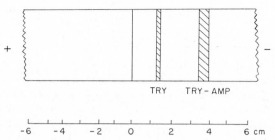

Fig. 2. Paper ionophoresis of tryptophan (TRY) and tryptophanyl adenylate (TRY-AMP) in 0.05 M ammonium formate buffer (pH 4.5); apparatus of Markham and Smith [11].

ganic pyrophosphate, and tris(hydroxymethyl) aminomethane buffer led to synthesis of adenosine triphosphate. Adenosine triphosphate was identified by coupling the reaction between radioactive inorganic pyrophosphate and tryptophanyl adenylate with the phosphorylation of glucose by hexokinase. The phosphate esters were separated by ethanol–barium salt fractionation, and radioactive glucose-6-phosphate was identified by paper chromatography in two solvent systems.

An experiment designed to demonstrate the net synthesis of tryptophanyl adenylate was carried out as follows. The total yield of tryptophan-activating enzyme obtained from 10 lb of beef pancreas (15 mg) was incubated with DL-tryptophan-3-C[14], magnesium chloride, crystalline pyrophosphatase, adenosine triphosphate, and tris(hydroxymethyl) aminomethane buffer for 30 minutes at 37° C. At the end of the incubation period, 2 mg of synthetic tryptophanyl adenylate was added as carrier and the reaction mixture was lyophilized. The lyophilized reaction mixture was fractionated according to the scheme shown in figure 3.

In the first step of this procedure, treatment with glacial acetic acid in the

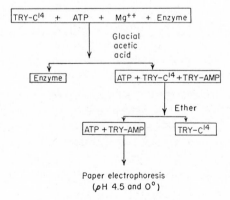

Fig. 3. Scheme for the isolation of tryptophanyl adenylate (TRY-AMP) from enzymatic reaction mixtures.

cold separated tryptophanyl adenylate from the enzyme which remained in the insoluble residue along with some magnesium chloride and tris(hydroxymethyl) aminomethane buffer. Subsequent addition of ether to the acetic acid extract resulted in the precipitation of adenosine triphosphate and tryptophanyl adenylate, leaving radioactive tryptophan in the supernatant solution. The precipitate, which contained both adenosine triphosphate and tryptophanyl adenylate, was washed several times with cold ether–glacial acetic acid followed by several ether extractions in order to remove residual acetic acid. The precipitate was dissolved in a small amount of ammonium formate buffer (pH 4.5), and an aliquot of this material was analyzed ionophoretically. The paper ionophoretic separation yielded a major radioactive band which corresponded in mobility to authentic tryptophanyl adenylate. A smaller band, negatively charged, was detected but has not yet been identified. The positively charged band was eluted, treated with hydroxylamine, and chromatographed on paper in several solvent systems. Radioactive tryptophan hydroxamic acid was identified in each system.

A similar experiment carried out without the addition of carrier tryptophanyl adenylate was also performed. Ionophoretic analysis again revealed evidence for the formation of tryptophanyl adenylate; however, somewhat less radioactivity was found in the tryptophanyl adenylate area. These findings suggested that there was incorporation of radioactive tryptophan into tryptophanyl adenylate in the experiment with carrier. In order to investigate this possibility directly, radioactive tryptophan was incubated with tryptophanyl adenylate, enzyme, and magnesium ions. The tryptophan hydroxamate isolated from this reaction mixture (after the addition of hydroxylamine) contained appreciable radioactivity; the findings therefore suggest that an exchange between tryptophan and tryptophanyl adenylate occurred:

$$TRY\text{-}C^{14} + TRY\text{-}AMP \rightarrow TRY\text{-}C^{14}\text{-}AMP + TRY$$

We have also found that the tryptophan-activating enzyme catalyzes the formation of adenosine triphosphate from inorganic pyrophosphate and a variety of α-aminoacyl adenylates. Thus, aminoacyl adenylates of L- and D-tryptophan, L- and D-phenylalanine, L-isoleucine, L-glutamine, L-alanine, glycine, L-proline, L-valine, L-leucine, and L-tyrosine gave adenosine triphosphate in this system. It is of some interest that D- and L-tryptophanyl adenylate and D- and L-phenylalanyl adenylate were about equally active. Examination of the D-anhydrides (after hydrolysis) by optically specific enzymatic methods [12] revealed that the optical purity of the amino acid moieties was greater than 99.5 per cent; it is therefore unlikely that the activity of the D-aminoacyl adenylate is due to the presence of adenylate derivatives of the corresponding enantiomorphs. Of the aminoacyl adenylates examined, only those of α-amino acids were active.[4]

---

[4] We have recently found that L-tryptophanyl inosinate [10] is inactive, and that inosine triphosphate is not active in place of adenosine triphosphate in the forward reaction (reaction 1, table 2).

Thus, carbobenzoxytryptophanyl adenylate, β-alanyl adenylate, and benzoyl adenylate were inactive (table 1). Table 2 summarizes some of the reactions catalyzed by the tryptophan-activating enzyme preparation. Under the conditions employed, the enzyme catalyzed the formation of L-tryptophan hydroxamate, but not that of the D isomer. This is in striking contrast to the results obtained on the synthesis of adenosine triphosphate (table 1). Further studies of the specificity of the enzyme system are in progress.

TABLE 1. Specificity of the Tryptophan-Activating Enzyme with Respect to Acyl Adenylate in Synthesis of Adenosine Triphosphate

Acyl Adenylates

Active	Inactive
L-Tryptophan-AMP	β-Alanine-AMP
D-Tryptophan-AMP	Acetyl-AMP
L-Phenylalanine-AMP	Benzoyl-AMP
D-Phenylalanine-AMP	Carbobenzoxytryptophan-AMP
L-Glutamine-AMP	Phenylacetyl-AMP
L-Isoleucine-AMP	
L-Leucine-AMP	
L-Valine-AMP	
L-Alanine-AMP	
L-Tyrosine-AMP	
Glycine-AMP	
L-Proline-AMP	
L-Threonine-AMP	
L-Serine-AMP	

TABLE 2. Types of Reactions Catalyzed by Tryptophan-Activating Enzyme

	Reaction Type	Specificity		
		L		D
(1)	$TRY + ATP + NH_2OH$	+		0
(2)	TRY-AMP + PP	+		+
(3)	L-TRY-AMP + DL-TRY-C^{14}		+ *	
(4)	Amino acid + ATP + NH_2OH	0		0
(5)	Amino acid-AMP + PP	+		+

* Studies with D- and L-TRY-C^{14} are not yet complete.

Note Added in Proof

Novelli [*Proc. Natl. Acad. Sci. U. S.*, *44*, 86 (1958)] has very recently reported synthesis of adenosine triphosphate from pyrophosphate and several aminoacyl adenylates with this enzyme, and Berg [*Federation Proc.*, *16*, 152 (1957); personal communication] has made similar observations with a methionine-activating enzyme obtained from yeast. Rhodes and McElroy (personal communication) have recently observed enzymatic synthesis of adenyl oxyluciferin by firefly luciferase; they have also obtained evidence for tight binding of this intermediate to the enzyme.

Recent studies in our laboratory indicate that the affinity of the tryptophan-activating enzyme is greater for L-tryptophanyl adenylate than for D-tryptophanyl adenylate and a number of the other α-aminoacyl adenylates listed in table 1.

REFERENCES

1. P. Berg, *J. Biol. Chem.*, *222*, 1015 (1956).

2. W. P. Jencks and F. Lipmann, *J. Biol. Chem.*, *225*, 207 (1957).

3. H. S. Moyed and F. Lipmann, *J. Bacteriol.*, *73*, 117 (1957).

4. K. Moldave and A. Meister, *J. Biol. Chem.*, *229*, 463 (1957).

5. M. B. Hoagland, E. B. Keller, and P. C. Zamecnik, *J. Biol. Chem.*, *218*, 345 (1956).

6. P. Berg, *J. Biol. Chem.*, *222*, 1025 (1956).

7. E. W. Davie, V. V. Koningsberger, and F. Lipmann, *Arch. Biochem. Biophys.*, *65*, 21 (1956).

8. J. A. DeMoss and G. D. Novelli, *Biochim. et Biophys. Acta*, *22*, 49 (1956).

9. M. B. Hoagland, P. C. Zamecnik, N. Sharon, F. Lipmann, M. P. Stulberg, and P. D. Boyer, *Biochim. et Biophys. Acta*, *26*, 215 (1957).

10. P. Castelfranco, A. Meister, and K. Moldave, paper 14 of this volume.

11. R. Markham and J. B. Smith, *Biochem. J.*, *52*, 552 (1952).

12. A. Meister, L. Levintow, R. M. Kingsley, and J. P. Greenstein, *J. Biol Chem.*, *192*, 535 (1951).

14

Participation of Adenyl Amino Acids in Amino Acid Incorporation into Proteins[1]

PAUL CASTELFRANCO[2]   ALTON MEISTER   KIVIE MOLDAVE

Department of Biochemistry, Tufts University School of Medicine

It has been postulated that aminoacyl adenylates possessing the general structure shown in figure 1 are formed in the enzymatic activation of amino acids

$$R - \underset{\underset{NH_3^+}{|}}{\overset{\overset{H}{|}}{C}} - \underset{}{\overset{\overset{O}{\parallel}}{C}} - O - \underset{\underset{O^-}{|}}{\overset{\overset{O}{\parallel}}{P}} - O - \text{Ribose} - \text{Adenine}^+$$

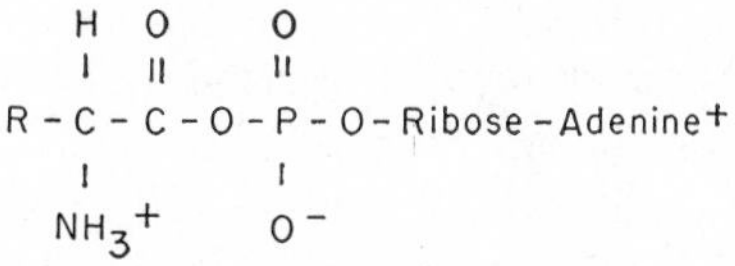

Fig. 1

by adenosine triphosphate, and that such "activated amino acids" are intermediates in the incorporation of amino acids into microsomal proteins observed in cell-free systems [1, 2]. Whether such incorporation represents protein synthesis is not yet known, although this hypothesis has indeed been considered. Recent studies in our laboratory have been directed toward a better understanding of the activation of amino acids and the possible role of aminoacyl adenylates in amino acid incorporation into protein. In the preceding paper by Karasek et al. [3], evidence for the net synthesis of tryptophanyl adenylate by a purified tryptophan-activating enzyme is described. These observations appear to give direct support to the idea that aminoacyl adenylates are the initial products of the activation reaction. The subsequent reactions of aminoacyl adenylates are not yet clearly understood, although it has been suggested that the amino acid moieties of such anhydrides are transferred to protein via specific acceptors, possibly ribonucleic acid [4].

[1] Supported in part by research grants from the National Science Foundation and the National Institutes of Health, Public Health Service.
[2] Postdoctorate fellow of the National Heart Institute, Public Health Service.

We began this work by attempting to prepare a number of aminoacyl adenylates in a reasonable state of purity and in good yield in order to make possible the synthesis of radioactive aminoacyl adenylates. It is not unusual in modern biochemical research to synthesize and study compounds that are believed to be intermediates in biochemical reactions. In the present instance this approach may suffer from a possible difficulty in that the intermediates may be bound to enzymes and therefore not be in equilibrium with an external source of intermediate. It has been observed, however, that chemically synthesized acyl adenylate derivatives are enzymatically active in systems that catalyze activation of acetate [5] and fatty acids [6, 7] and the synthesis of phenylacetyl-glutamine and hippurate [8].

Two procedures have been described for the preparation of aminoacyl adenylates. One of these [9] involves the condensation of the acid chloride of an amino acid with silver adenylate. DeMoss et al. [9] obtained leucyl adenylate in 9 per cent yield by this procedure. The other method involves condensation of the free amino acid and adenylic acid in the presence of N,N'-dicyclohexylcarbodiimide, and precipitation of the product by addition of acetone [2]. In our hands, these methods suffered from shortcomings often encountered in the attempted synthesis of highly reactive molecules; thus, we obtained very low yields of products of very low purity, and experienced great difficulty in attempts at purification of the anhydrides.

In an effort to solve these problems, we investigated a number of synthetic approaches, two of which have proved successful. The first consisted of condensing an N-carbobenzoxyamino acid anhydride with adenylic acid in aqueous pyridine; the N-carbobenzoxyaminoacyl adenylate was isolated, and the blocking group was removed by catalytic hydrogenation with palladium [10].

Subsequently, an alternative synthesis was developed which has proved to be more convenient; it will therefore be described here in greater detail. Equimolar quantities of N-carbobenzoxyamino acid and adenylic acid were shaken in aqueous pyridine with an excess of N,N'-dicyclohexylcarbodiimide for several hours. N,N'-Dicyclohexylurea was removed by filtration, and the filtrate was treated with acetone to precipitate the product. Treatment with acetone removed unreacted N-carbobenzoxyamino acid, N,N'-dicyclohexylcarbodiimide, and most of the pyridine and water. The precipitate was extracted with ethylene glycol monomethyl ether; the product is soluble, and adenylic acid is insoluble in this solvent. The N-carbobenzoxyaminoacyl adenylate was precipitated from the extract by addition of ether. After catalytic hydrogenation of the carbobenzoxy compound and removal of the catalyst, the supernatant solution was lyophilized. The free aminoacyl adenylate was obtained as a white powder.

The yields varied from 40 to 80 per cent; for example, glycyl-1-C^{14}-adenylate was obtained in 75 per cent yield, and the yield of DL-tryptophanyl-3-C^{14}-adenylate was 44 per cent. The final products are estimated to be 70 to 80 per cent pure on the basis of the hydroxamic acid–ferric chloride color reaction [11]. The major impurities consist of adenylic acid and amino acid formed by hydrolysis of the anhydride during hydrogenation. This method has been successfully applied to the following amino acids: glycine, alanine, valine, leucine, isoleucine, β-alanine, proline, phenylalanine, tyrosine, tryptophan, glutamine, asparagine, threonine, methionine, and serine. Studies on the remaining natural amino acids are in progress.

Evidence for the proposed anhydride structure (fig. 1) includes the following: (*a*) hydrolysis in alkaline solution yields equivalent quantities of adenylic acid and amino acid; (*b*) reaction with hydroxylamine yields the corresponding amino acid hydroxamates, which have been identified by paper chromatography; and (*c*) paper ionophoretic study indicates that the aminoacyl adenylates have a net positive charge at *p*H 4.5. The possibility that the carboxyl group of the amino acid may be linked to the adenylic acid moiety through a group (e.g., 6-amino group of adenine) other than the phosphoric acid group appears unlikely in view of the unusual reactivity of these compounds.[3] An additional property of α-aminoacyl adenylates which has proved of value in characterization is their reactivity in the presence of the tryptophan-activating enzyme and inorganic pyrophosphate to yield adenosine triphosphate [3].

α-Aminoacyl adenylates are very labile in aqueous solution at values of *p*H above 5.5. Thus, at *p*H 7.2 at 37° C, they exhibited half-lives of 5 to 10 minutes. On the other hand, carbobenzoxyaminoacyl adenylates suffered only about 10 to 20 per cent hydrolysis in 2 hours at 37° at *p*H 7.2. Acetyl adenylate and benzoyl adenylate exhibit stability of approximately the same order as carbobenzoxyaminoacyl adenylates under these conditions.

Preparation of glycyl-C^{14}-adenylate and tryptophanyl-C^{14}-adenylate made it possible to study incorporation of the respective amino acid moieties into proteins in systems previously employed for studies of amino acid incorporation. The enzyme preparation was obtained as described by Zamecnik and Keller [12]; it consisted of the supernatant solution (containing microsomes) obtained by centrifuging a 25 per cent rat liver homogenate at 12,000*g*. This preparation catalyzed the incorporation of amino acids into microsomal proteins in the presence of adenosine triphosphate and an adenosine triphosphate–

---

[3] Additional evidence for the proposed structure has recently been obtained. Thus, we have been able to convert carbobenzoxytryptophanyl adenylate with nitrous acid to the corresponding inosinic acid derivative. The latter compound has also been prepared by condensing inosinic acid with N-carbobenzoxytryptophan by the procedure described in the text for anhydrides of adenylic acid.

Acylation of the hydroxyl groups of ribose appears to be excluded. Thus, carbobenzoxyaminoacyl adenylates consumed theoretical quantities of periodate and, after reaction with periodate, reacted with hydroxylamine to give the corresponding carbobenzoxyamino acid hydroxamates. Paper ionophoretic study of the carbobenzoxyaminoacyl adenylates in borate and other buffers was also consistent with the presence of free ribose hydroxyl groups; the mobility of these compounds (and of adenylic acid) was greater in borate buffer than in tris(hydroxymethyl) aminomethane buffer at *p*H 9.1.

generating system. Thus, in the system of Zamecnik and Keller [12], we observed 57 and 81 cpm/mg protein, respectively, with glycine-1-C^{14} and tryptophan-3-C^{14}. As is indicated in table 1, incubation of the enzyme preparation with radioactive glycyl adenylate resulted in significant incorporation of isotope into the protein subsequently isolated. When the anhydride was hydrolyzed with alkali before study, significant incorporation was not observed. Furthermore, equimolar concentrations of radioactive glycine plus adenylic acid did not lead to incorporation. It should be emphasized that the specific activities of the C^{14}-aminoacyl adenylates were 5 per cent of the values for the free amino acids used by us in the system of Zamecnik and Keller.

TABLE 1. Incorporation Studies

Reaction Mixtures *	cpm/mg
Enzyme + Glycine-1-C^{14} + Adenylate	0.17
Enzyme + Glycyl-1-C^{14}-adenylate	17.1
Enzyme † + Glycyl-1-C^{14}-adenylate	195.
Enzyme † + Glycine-1-C^{14} + Adenylate	1.31

* The reaction mixtures contained enzyme (1 ml) and glycyl-C^{14}-adenylate (2.5 μmoles; 3.6×10^5 cpm) in a final volume of 2.5 ml; incubated at 38° for 30 minutes. Similar results were obtained when concentrations of aminoacyl adenylate from 10^{-2} M to $10^{-6}M$ were employed.

† Enzyme heated at 100° for 10 minutes.

Although these results appeared to be consistent with the hypothesis that aminoacyl adenylates are intermediates in the incorporation of amino acids into proteins, further experiments have raised the possibility that such incorporation may be explained in terms of nonenzymatic acylation of protein. Thus, it was found that, when the enzyme preparation was heated for 10 minutes at 100° before incubation with C^{14}-aminoacyl adenylate, the incorporation of isotope into protein was considerably greater than with the unheated enzyme preparation. In the experiments with heated enzyme, appreciable incorporation of isotope did not occur with hydrolyzed anhydride preparations. Similar results have been obtained with tryptophanyl-C^{14}-adenylate.

With both heated and unheated enzyme preparations, the binding of the incorporated amino acid to protein was quite stable and could be released only by the drastic acid hydrolysis required for the cleavage of peptide bonds. Thus, with glycine-1-C^{14}–labeled protein (heated and unheated), the quantity of free amino acids and the percentage of isotope released as $C^{14}O_2$ by ninhydrin increased in parallel fashion during hydrolysis with 6 N HCl at 105° over a period of 16 hours. When the proteins labeled by incubation with glycyl-1-C^{14}-adenylate and with tryptophanyl-3-C^{14}-adenylate were treated with 1-fluoro-2,4-dinitrobenzene, followed by acid hydrolysis, dinitrophenylamino acid preparations were obtained which contained more than 70 per cent of the radioactivity originally incorporated into the protein. Similar results were obtained with heated and unheated enzyme preparations.

We have also found that, when glycyl-1-C^{14}-adenylate is incubated with purified rat-liver ribonucleic acid obtained by phenol extraction [13], considerable radioactivity remains associated with the ribonucleic acid preparation after exhaustive dialysis and ethanol precipitation. Approximately 40 per cent of the radioactivity of the ribonucleic acid preparation was alkali-labile. When such ribonucleic acid preparations were incubated with unheated and heated protein preparations, significant quantities of radioactivity were found in the protein subsequently isolated. Thus, incubation of 1 micromole of glycyl-1-C^{14}-adenylate with 50 mg of liver ribonucleic acid in 1 ml of water for 30 minutes at 38° gave a ribonucleic acid preparation containing 3000 cpm (after dialysis and precipitation). When 20 mg of this C^{14}-ribonucleic acid (1500 cpm) was incubated with enzyme preparation (table 1) for 30 minutes at 38°, approximately 100 cpm was associated with the protein subsequently isolated. Similar results were obtained with heated enzyme preparation.

The observed reactions of the aminoacyl adenylates with proteins are consistent with the reactivity expected of anhydrides of this type. A similar result might occur when proteins are treated with radioactive acetic anhydride. The reaction of the aminoacyl adenylates with the heated protein preparations would appear to be a nonenzymatic acylation reaction involving the free reactive groups of proteins. Heat denaturation of the protein would be expected to expose a greater number of amino groups to the action of the acylating agents.[4] The extent to which the labeling observed with unheated proteins may be due to an enzymatic mechanism is not known. Although we believe that in the present studies transfer of the amino acid moieties from aminoacyl adenylates to proteins occurred largely by a nonenzymatic process, the possibility cannot be excluded that some of this transfer is enzymatically catalyzed. Perhaps nonenzymatic acylation of proteins may also take place to some extent when amino acids are incubated with adenosine triphosphate, an adenosine triphosphate–generating system, and a suitable enzyme preparation. The aminoacyl adenylates formed in the activation reaction [3] might be expected to react in such a manner. Thus, the high reactivity of aminoacyl adenylates with protein and ribonucleic acid may explain at least some of the reported [4, 12] incorporation phenomena.

It must be emphasized that the concentrations of aminoacyl adenylates presumably formed in the amino acid incorporation systems previously studied would be expected to be considerably lower than the concentrations of aminoacyl adenylates we have used. Much lower concentrations of aminoacyl adenylates than those used here must be employed to make a meaningful comparison of the labeling in the two systems. Such studies will require aminoacyl adenylates of considerably higher specific radioactivity. Although the present investigations raise the possibility that incorporation in cell-free systems into

---

[4] Porter [14] has reported that heat denaturation of several proteins increases the number of ε-amino groups of lysine that can react with acylating agents.

microsomal protein may be at least to some extent nonenzymatic, it is quite possible that physiological mechanisms exist for the controlled transfer of the amino acid moieties of aminoacyl adenylates.

Note Added in Proof

Zioudrou, Fujii, and Fruton have recently described the synthesis of C^{14}-tyrosinyl adenylate and C^{14}-glycyltyrosinyl adenylate by a procedure similar to ours. They observed labeling of heated and unheated rat-liver mitochondria by these compounds and by their N-carbobenzoxy derivatives. They have also concluded that the labeling of the mitochondria is due to nonenzymatic acylation (personal communication from Dr. J. S. Fruton; *Proc. Natl. Acad. Sci. U. S.*, in press).

Further studies in our laboratory indicate that enzymatically synthesized tryptophanyl adenylate can acylate microsomal preparations and also other proteins (e.g., bovine serum albumin, ovalbumin); these experiments were carried out with systems containing pancreatic tryptophan-activating enzyme, ATP, magnesium ions, and acceptor protein. Labeling of ribonucleic acid preparations was also observed by such systems. The recent findings of Berg and Ofengand [15] and of Schweet, Bovard, Allen, and Glassman [16] are consistent with the possibility that specific binding sites for amino acids exist on soluble ribonucleic acid molecules. Whether such specific binding of amino acids to ribonucleic acid can be obtained with chemically synthesized aminoacyl adenylates remains to be determined. The present studies emphasize the importance of isolating specific proteins in experiments on protein biosynthesis; the recent report of Bates, Craddock, and Simpson [17] on the incorporation of valine into mitochondrial cytochrome c appears to be a significant step in this direction.

REFERENCES

1. M. B. Hoagland, E. B. Keller, and P. C. Zamecnik, *J. Biol. Chem.* 218, 345 (1956).

2. P. Berg, *Federation Proc.*, 16, 152 (1957).

3. M. Karasek, P. Castelfranco, P. R. Krishnaswamy, and A. Meister, paper 13 of this volume.

4. M. B. Hoagland, P. C. Zamecnik, and M. L. Stephenson, *Biochim. et Biophys. Acta*, 24, 215 (1957).

5. P. Berg, *J. Biol. Chem.*, 222, 1015 (1956).

6. W. P. Jencks and F. Lipmann, *J. Biol. Chem.*, 225, 207 (1957).

7. H. S. Moyed and F. Lipmann, *J. Bacteriol.*, 73, 117 (1957).

8. K. Moldave and A. Meister, *J. Biol. Chem.*, 229, 463 (1957).

9. J. A. DeMoss, S. M. Genuth, and G. D. Novelli, *Proc. Natl. Acad. Sci. U. S.*, 42, 325 (1956).

10. M. Bergmann and L. Zervas, *Ber.*, 67, 1192 (1932).

11. F. Lipmann and L. C. Tuttle, *J. Biol. Chem.*, 159, 21 (1945).

12. P. C. Zamecnik and E. G. Keller, *J. Biol. Chem.*, 209, 337 (1954).

13. A. Gierer and G. Schramm, *Nature*, 177, 702 (1956).

14. R. R. Porter, *Biochim. et Biophys. Acta*, 2, 105 (1948).

15. P. Berg and E. J. Ofengand, *Proc. Natl. Acad. Sci. U. S.*, 44, 78 (1958).

16. R. S. Schweet, F. C. Bovard, E. Allen, and E. Glassman, *Proc. Natl. Acad. Sci. U. S.*, 44, 173 (1958).

17. H. M. Bates, V. M. Craddock, and M. V. Simpson, *J. Am. Chem. Soc.*, 80, 1000 (1958).

15

The Synthesis of Hydroxyproline
within Osteoblasts
[Abstract]

SYLVIA FITTON JACKSON

Medical Research Council Biophysics Research Unit
Wheatstone Laboratory, King's College, London

Biochemical and morphological methods are being used to study the stages of synthesis of intercellular material in active collagen-producing tissue cultures. The direct oxidation of proline already bound in peptide linkage may be an important step in the sequence of the synthetic processes which lead to the formation of collagen protein [Stetten, 1949]. In previous work it has been found that appreciable amounts of protein-bound hydroxyproline were formed during the first 24 hr of culture before the appearance of characteristic collagen fibrils [Fitton Jackson and Smith, 1957]. Free C^{14}-L-proline was also readily incorporated into the proteins of the growing tissue, and as much as 20 per cent was converted to protein-bound C^{14}-hydroxyproline [Smith and Fitton Jackson, 1957].

Cell fractionation studies have been made on similar tissue cultures in an attempt to establish whether the site of incorporation of free proline into the proteins of the cell was the same as that of the formation of the protein-bound hydroxyproline. The cultures were grown in contact with C^{14}-L-proline for various times and subsequently homogenized and subjected to differential centrifugation in 0.88 M sucrose solution. The amount of labeled proline incorporated and converted to hydroxyproline in the six isolated fractions was measured. Observations were made in parallel on the morphology of the whole cells and the various cellular fractions by means of the electron microscope.

Chemical analyses demonstrated the consistent presence of protein-bound hydroxyproline in the fractions of larger particle size (3000 A). The results also showed that, under the influence of the cells, free C^{14}-L-proline was most rapidly incorporated into the proteins of the supernatant (obtained after final centrifugation), and into the "small-granule" fraction of the cytoplasm (sedimented at 105,000g); these fractions also contained the greatest amount of ribose. Subsequently part of the labeled proline appeared as hydroxyproline in a large-granule fraction (~3000 A particle size) as well as in fractions of larger particle size; for example, after 21 hours of culture growth followed by contact with radioactive proline for 1 hr it was found that for every 100 residues of protein-bound proline 16.9 residues were hydroxylated in this fraction. With longer contact times the radioactivity of the larger-granule fractions increased considerably.

The significance of these results in relation to the synthesis of collagen protein by the osteoblasts and in the mechanism of the formation of typical collagen fibrils was discussed.

REFERENCES

M. R. Stetten, 1949, *J. Biol. Chem., 181*, 31.

S. Fitton Jackson and R. H. Smith, 1957, *J. Biophys. Biochem. Cytol., 3*, 679.

R. H. Smith and S. Fitton Jackson, 1957, *J. Biophys. Biochem. Cytol., 3*, 692.

16

Studies on Amino Acid Incorporation in Bacteria Using Ionizing Radiation

ELLIS KEMPNER   ERNEST POLLARD

Biophysics Department, Yale University [1]

In recent years a growing body of evidence supports the idea that ribonucleo-protein particles form at least one of the sites of protein synthesis [1]. Evidence regarding this highly interesting system can be obtained by working with cell-free systems of purified particles, and undoubtedly such evidence is valuable and convincing. The drastic destruction of cell organization which is involved, how-ever, leaves the question that perhaps the whole nature of amino acid incor-poration is not being observed, but only the part that can survive the disrup-tion of order in the cell. A method of study having the great advantage that the cell is intact, or very nearly so, throughout the whole process is the use of ionizing radiation as a powerful local disruptive agent. Such radiation is able to penetrate all parts of the cell; it acts only at single, nearly isolated points, and is wholly without action elsewhere. Such high-energy spot probes, or line probes, can be employed against the organization of the cell, and, from the effect on any particular part of the synthetic process, deductions can be made regarding the process itself. Under good conditions, information can be ob-tained on the following points: (*a*) the approximate size (within a factor of 2 in volume) of the region concerned with synthesis and sensitive to radiation; (*b*) the approximate thickness (within a factor of 2 or 3), and hence the ap-proximate length; and (*c*) the sensitivity of the synthetic region to radiation (within a factor of 2). These data can be compared with the sizes, thicknesses, and lengths of cellular elements that could take part in the synthetic process. This comparison can then be used as one more piece of evidence regarding the nature of the process. A start along this line of investigation was made by

[1] Aided by a grant from the John A. Hartford Foundation.

123

Hutchinson, Morowitz, and Kempner [2]. If sources of radiation are available, the method is, relatively speaking, technically easy, and therefore attractive. It is necessary, however, to be aware of the uncertainties of interpretation, to be sure that misleading deductions have not been made. The use of ionizing radiation to study cellular processes has been under intensive study in this laboratory for several years [2, 3, 4, 5, 6], and therefore a summary of the findings seems worth while, so that the validity of the conclusions can be estimated.

The two major classes of biological macromolecules, proteins and nucleic acids, appear to be very sensitive to ionizing radiation. An enzyme molecule loses its activity if a cluster of ions forms anywhere inside the molecule; an antigenic protein loses its ability to combine with antibody if such a cluster forms in a volume somewhat smaller than that of the protein. DNA, as transforming principle, loses its function if such a cluster forms within a unit of about 300,000 molecular weight. If irradiations are carried out in solution, reaction products can move around, and they may have marked inactivating power. Studies by Hutchinson [7] on yeast cells in various conditions of moisture indicate that in the cell such reaction products carry their effectiveness over a distance of only 30 A. All these effects can be modified by factors of about 2 by several environmental conditions, notably oxygen tension and degree of aggregation between protein molecules. Thus, until the final sorting out of cause and effect is accomplished, the statistical interpretation of radiation effects must be considered to be approximate only. Even so, it is valuable as an aid in studying an important, inaccessible process. To give some idea of the validity of the conclusions drawn we reproduce here a diagram, prepared by W. R. Guild, showing the relation between the "target molecular weight" derived from the statistical radiation analysis of radiation inactivation and the accepted molecular weights. Since the diagram is a log-log plot, it should not be viewed over-optimistically, but the reason can be seen for the claim that a factor of 2 is normally all that is involved as error.

In order to gain the maximum information from irradiation studies, at least three, and preferably more, types of irradiation should be carried out: (1) Irradiation by radiation sources very rich in fast electrons, as, for example, electrons themselves, of energy 0.5 Mev or more, or γ-ray sources of energy in excess of 1 Mev, where the secondary electrons due to Compton recoil and photoelectric absorption have energies, in the main, in excess of 0.5 Mev. (2) Irradiation by heavy particles of variable rates of energy loss. Such particles have dense ionization, largely confined to tracks, and they give a different distribution of local energy releases from fast electrons. Heavy particles of at least two energies should be used, to give a range of separation of energy releases. In our experiments we have employed cobalt 60 γ radiation, deuterons of varied energies, and α particles as bombarding agents. The results show that the uptake of methionine into the protein fraction (fraction insoluble in cold trichloroacetic acid) is retained unless very heavy irradiations are employed, and the sensitive region fits very well with a sphere of radius 130 A. For the uptake of proline into the

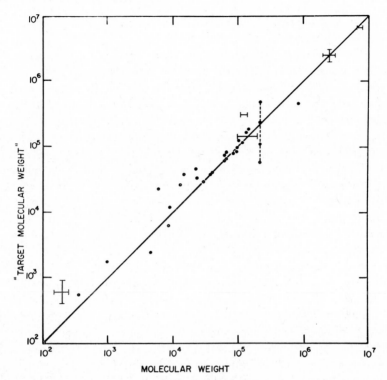

Fig. 1. Comparison of accepted molecular weights and those determined by target analysis. We wish to thank W. R. Guild of our laboratory for permission to use this figure.

same fraction the same analysis cannot hold; instead, the best fit to the data is found for a long, thin, sensitive volume of radius roughly 11 A and length roughly 2.2 microns. Thus the methionine incorporation can very well be identified with a process taking place in a microsomal particle, usually estimated as having a radius of 100 A [8], while the proline incorporation appears to implicate a whole chain, probably of nucleic acid, and may mean that the incorporation of proline is dependent on the integrity of a system that binds together several microsomal particles. The experiments forming the basis for these conclusions can now be described.

MATERIALS AND METHODS

Cultures of *Escherichia coli* B, maintained in this laboratory for a year, were grown with aeration at 37° C in an inorganic salt medium ("Minimal C medium" [9]) containing 5 g of glucose per liter. Aeration was stopped when the bacteria reached a concentration of approximately 5×10^8 cells/ml as read in a Bausch and Lomb spectrophotometer. This is about the middle of the logarithmic-growth phase in this medium. The cells had a generation time of about 50 minutes.

Cobalt 60 irradiation: Twenty-milliliter samples of bacteria were sealed in culture tubes and placed in a cobalt 60 source which delivered 380,000 r/hour. The temperature in the source was approximately 30° C. After irradiation, the tubes were placed unopened in a 37° C water bath, and allowed to rise to that temperature.

Cyclotron bombardment: Bacterial cells were spun down in a Sorvall Model SS-1 centrifuge, and the pellet was resuspended at a concentration of 1×10^{10} cells/ml in minimal medium with no glucose added. One-tenth milliliter of this suspension was placed on fine-pore filters (Millipore Filter Corporation) and kept moist with a coarse filter backing containing distilled water. Irradiation was performed in air at 0° C [10]. After irradiation, the bacteria were resuspended in 10 ml of minimal medium with no glucose and allowed to come to 37° C.

After irradiation and temperature equilibration, the bacterial suspension was added to an equal volume of minimal medium containing glucose which was aerated at 37° C. This incubation mixture contained 0.2 μc of the radioisotope to be studied. L-Methionine-S^{35}, 5.5 mc/g, and L-cystine-S^{35}, 14.5 mc/g, were obtained from the Abbott Laboratories, Oak Ridge. L-Proline-C^{14}, 8.9 mc/mM; L-leucine-C^{14}, 7.95 mc/mM; and D-glucose-C^{14}, 2.06 μc/mg, were supplied by the Nuclear-Chicago Corporation. At various times during the incubation, 2-ml samples were taken for the "whole cell" and "TCA-insoluble" fractions [2]. The filters on which these fractions were placed were then dried in air and counted under a thin window (less than 150 μg/cm²) Geiger-Müller counter. Background was about 17 counts per minute.

In order to provide the variety in distribution of ionization densities as mentioned in the introduction, cyclotron bombardments were carried out with various thicknesses of aluminum absorber between the bacteria and the beam. Since the beam has a definite range, the amount of inactivation it produced varied with the absorbers, falling to zero when the range in absorber was exceeded, so that no deuterons hit the bacteria. From these curves the equivalent absorption of each bacterial preparation could be measured and thus the effective energy of the deuterons hitting them estimated. Since the density of ionization varies with energy in a known way [5], the appropriate value for each bombardment can be determined.

RESULTS

The effect of irradiation with cobalt 60 on the uptake of L-methionine is shown in figure 2. Three sets of curves are presented. The first, on the left, applies to the uptake of unirradiated *E. coli*. The counts per minute are plotted against time for two samplings: the whole cell, as represented by the upper line, and the fraction insoluble in cold trichloroacetic acid (TCA). The differ-

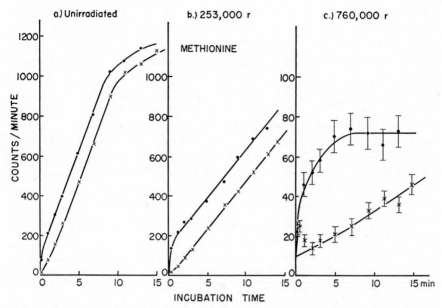

Fig. 2. The effect of γ radiation on methionine incorporation in *E. coli*. Except where otherwise marked in these figures, solid circles correspond to the label in the intact cell, and crosses refer to the cold-TCA-insoluble fraction. The difference between these two curves, the "pool," is seen to decrease with increasing dose of radiation. Background was 20 cpm and has been subtracted.

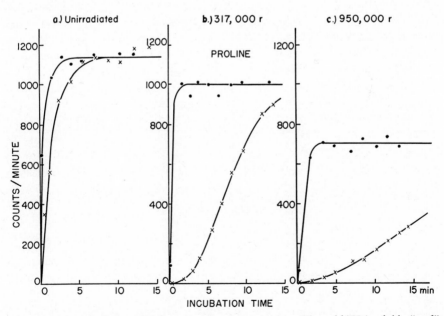

Fig. 3. The effect of γ radiation on proline incorporation. The cold-TCA-soluble "pool" rises in magnitude and then falls off with dose.

ence between these two, following Britten, Roberts, and French [11] and Cohen and Rickenberg [12], is designated as the metabolic pool. In figure 2*b,* the same process is employed on bacteria that have received 253,000 roentgens of cobalt 60 irradiation. It can be seen that the total amount of radioactivity incorporated in the TCA-insoluble fraction is reduced; the rate of incorporation is also less. The amount taken up by the whole cells is less, though not quite to the same extent as the reduction in the TCA-insoluble fraction. In figure 2*c,* still higher irradiation was employed, and the reductions in both fractions are still more apparent.

Similar data are shown in figure 3 for the uptake of proline. There is a marked difference from the effects with methionine in that more irradiation is necessary to reduce the amount incorporated into any fraction, about twice the dose in the TCA-insoluble fraction and nearly 10 times in the whole-cell fraction. Because of the disparity in these effects it can be seen that the pool actually rises after bombardment.

For these two amino acids, with the exception of the proline pool, the amount of activity remaining seems to be a diminishing exponential function of the dose. The data scatter somewhat, but we have no real evidence in favor of a multiple-hit type of process, where the activity remains nearly constant and then rapidly falls. The per cent remaining activity for methionine incorporation is plotted against dose in figure 4. For proline incorporation the effect of radiation is definitely less in the TCA-insoluble fraction than for methionine, and very markedly less in the whole-cell case. Such dose effect curves can be analyzed statistically in terms of an inactivation volume V, which is the sensitive region that must escape an ionization in order to retain the effect being measured. If the ionizations occur at a number I per unit volume, then the average number of ionizations occurring in the sensitive region is IV, and by the Poisson relation the probability that the region will escape is e^{-IV}. Thus the natural logarithm of the ratio remaining to that in the unirradiated control should be $-IV$. For 37 per cent remaining, the value of IV is unity.

Table 1 summarizes the results of cobalt 60 studies. The first column gives the 37 per cent dose found from the survival curves. The second column gives the corresponding number of primary ionizations per cubic centimeter for such a dose. Column three, the sensitive volume, is the reciprocal of the value in

TABLE 1. Summary of Incorporation Studies in the TCA-Insoluble Fraction of *E. coli* Irradiated with Cobalt 60 γ Rays

	37% Dose, r	Primary Ionizations per cm³	Sensitive Volume, cm³	Equivalent Spherical Radius, A
Leucine C¹⁴	0.36×10^6	1.8×10^{17}	5.6×10^{-18}	110
Cystine S³⁵	0.45×10^6	2.3×10^{17}	4.3×10^{-18}	100
Methionine S³⁵	0.20×10^6	1.0×10^{17}	10.0×10^{-18}	130
Proline C¹⁴	0.45×10^6	2.3×10^{17}	4.3×10^{-18}	100
Glucose C¹⁴	0.84×10^6	4.3×10^{17}	2.3×10^{-18}	82

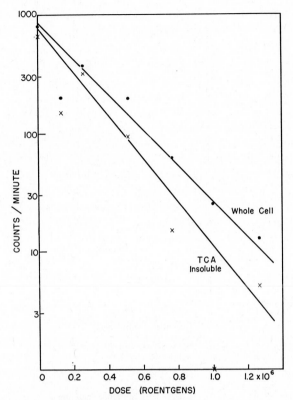

Fig. 4. Survival of methionine incorporation with γ-ray dose. The ordinate is on a logarithmic scale. Pool fraction shows similar survival.

the second column. The last column, the "equivalent spherical radius," is the value calculated assuming that the sensitive volume is the shape of a sphere; it is listed for comparative purposes only.

Cyclotron irradiations produced similar effects. The data scatter even more, probably owing to the difficulty in securing irradiations involving the same time of exposure on the Millipore filter. There is quite clear evidence of a reduction in activity, as can be seen from figure 5, where the uptake of methionine is shown for control and two irradiated points. Uptake curves of the sulfur-labeled amino acids do not extrapolate to zero counts per minute at zero time, owing to adsorption of the label, and this correction is deducted in plotting survival curves. Figure 6 shows analogous curves for proline incorporation, also after deuteron irradiation. These experiments were performed without added aluminum absorber in the cyclotron beam.

Similar studies were carried out with various absorbing foils, and, from the uptake curves, curves relating the per cent uptake remaining to the number of deuterons per square centimeter used to irradiate were drawn for each foil thickness. In each case, the 37 per cent dose (in deuterons per square centi-

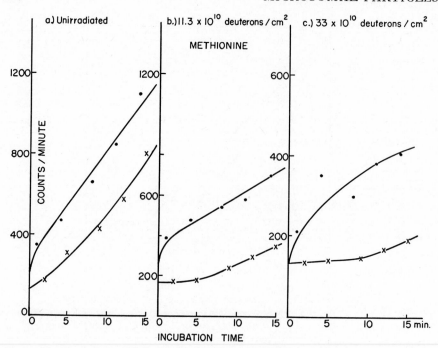

Fig. 5. The effect of deuteron bombardment on methionine incorporation. Count rate at zero time is due to adsorption of the label.

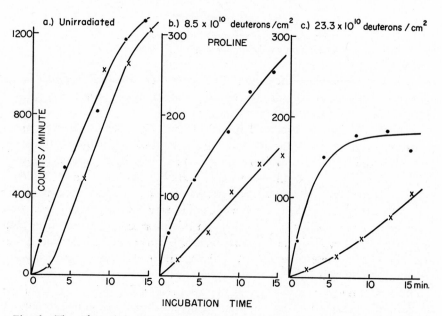

Fig. 6. The effect of deuteron bombardment on proline incorporation. Here the pool decreases in absolute magnitude with dose.

meter) was found. The statistical analysis is similar. If we assume that a deuteron is able to inactivate as long as it passes through the sensitive region, then the area of the sensitive region is all that matters. On that basis, if D is the number of deuterons per square centimeter and S is the area of the sensitive unit concerned with amino acid uptake, we see that the average number of deuterons per target is SD, and once again the probability of escape is e^{-SD}. Therefore at the value of D for 37 per cent remaining, $SD=1$. S is referred to as the "cross section." It must be remembered that a deuteron may not be perfectly efficient in producing inactivation, and in particular, if the ionizations have a finite separation, then a thin target can be "straddled." This effect is apparently present for proline uptake.

In figure 7, the cross section is plotted against the air equivalent of the foil thickness for the TCA-insoluble fraction containing C^{14} proline. The maximum of this curve is near 26×10^{-12} cm^2 at a value of 5.5 cm air equivalent of foil. From the residual range of the beam, the value of the linear energy transfer (LET) at this cross section is found to be 400 electron volts per 100 A.

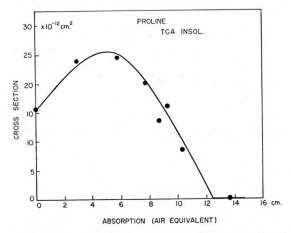

Fig. 7. Measured cross section for proline incorporation into the TCA-insoluble portion of *E. coli* after deuteron bombardment as a function of added aluminum in the cyclotron beam; 12.5 cm is seen to be the range of the deuteron beam in air.

Incorporation studies after α-particle bombardment are indicated in figure 8 for proline. The survival curves for such studies were reasonably exponential, with a 37 per cent dose for the TCA-insoluble portion labeled with proline of about 2.7×10^{10} α particles per cm^2.

The results of γ-ray, deuteron, and α-particle irradiations are combined in the LET plot [5] in figure 9. The two relations, in terms of volume V and area S, reduce to the same expression when the density of ionization, or linear energy transfer, is low. Under such circumstances, if i is the number of primary ionizations per unit length, $I=Di$, so that we obtain for the probability of escape e^{-DiV}, or $S=iV$. Thus the value of S close to the origin can be found

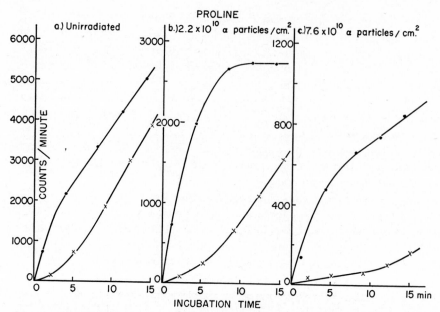

Fig. 8.   The effect of α-particle irradiation on proline incorporation. The pool decreases with increasing dose.

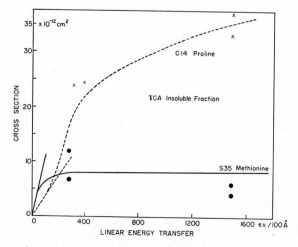

Fig. 9.   Measured cross sections for proline (crosses, dashed line) and methionine (solid circles, solid line) incorporation into the cold-TCA-insoluble fraction as a function of the rate of energy loss (LET). Slopes at the origin are calculated from γ-ray experiments as explained in the text.

by substituting the product of i and V as already found from irradiation with γ rays. Such a relation only applies close to the origin, but can be used to determine the initial slope. To a reasonable approximation, i is the energy loss per centimeter, in electron volts, divided by 110.

The slopes at the origin (dashed for proline, solid for methionine) are calculated from the sensitive volumes found with γ radiation. The points near 400 ev/100 A are from the deuteron experiments as described above. The LET for α particles in our experimental arrangement was 1500 ev/100 A, and the cross sections found by this method are shown at that LET value.

DISCUSSION

The analysis of the methionine–cold-TCA-insoluble fraction data indicates a spherical target. The radius calculated from the inactivation volume is 130 A; the radius calculated from the cross-sectional area is 127 A. The agreement is well within the uncertainties of this method of study.

The proline data are somewhat more complex. The upward concavity near the origin indicates a rather complex response to radiation. It can be explained most simply by supposing that closely grouped ionizations are more effective than single ionizations, and the rapid change of slope suggests that this multiplicity is small, probably a double ionization requirement [5]. There is no agreement between the area and volume determinations if a spherical target is assumed, no matter which ionization requirement (one, two, three, or four) is used. The only simple model that fits the data is a long, thin rod [10]. For a double ionization requirement, the volume and area determinations lead to a model of a rod of 11 A radius and 2.2 μ length. The analysis based upon the model of a thin plate leads to substantially the same result, an extremely long plate of small cross-sectional area.

Preliminary experiments with deuteron-bombarded *E. coli* cells indicate that the incorporation of glucose into the TCA-insoluble portion of these cells requires the integrity of a sphere of approximately 80 A radius. Since, in these experiments, glucose was the single carbon source available to the organisms, it seems reasonable to conclude that amino acids are produced in the cells in spheres of this size. Since the doses required to stop glucose incorporation into the cold-TCA-insoluble fraction are large compared with the doses required to stop exogenous methionine from being incorporated into the same fraction, it would appear that the formation of proteins from amino acids is not directly related to the incorporation of glucose. Further work on this very interesting result is clearly necessary.

If the two radiation-sensitive spheres found for glucose and methionine incorporation were assumed to have a density of 1.3, and to be sedimenting in a solution of viscosity 1.5 centipoises, then from

$$d^2 = 18\eta_s V/(1-V\rho)$$

it can be calculated that the spheres associated with glucose incorporation (160 A diameter) should have a sedimentation constant of the order of 25 S, while the larger, methionine-associated sphere, 260 A in diameter, should have a sedimentation constant of about 77 S. Since particles of such size have been reported in extracts of *E. coli* [13], our work can be interpreted as support for the functional character of these particles.

If the incorporation of exogenous amino acids into a TCA-insoluble form corresponds to protein synthesis, then the conclusion that at least two different amino acids are incorporated by two different structures within the cell logically leads to a model in which protein synthesis takes place in at least two steps. If the two units found by radiation were simultaneously required and both essential for protein synthesis, then methionine and proline would be expected to give the same radiation targets. The fact that targets of quite different character are found indicates that there must be some difference between the two. It is clearly interesting to continue the studies to see whether groupings of types of target exist.

Actually, that an ionization in a cellular unit which is probably composed of a dozen or so subunits should destroy its function is surprising. It seems certain that the effect of radiation on one part can precipitate a disruptive effect on the whole. This suggestion has already been made by Billen and Volkin [14]. Our data tend to support their conclusions.

ACKNOWLEDGMENTS

We wish to thank Messers P. Hanawalt, P. Schambra, and J. Lowry for assistance in running the cyclotron. We are also grateful to Drs. R. Roberts, D. Cowie, R. Britten, and E. Bolton for advice in rapid filtration procedures as well as for many stimulating discussions.

SUMMARY

Ionizing radiations of different character, γ rays, deuterons, and α particles, were used to determine radiation targets for the incorporation of methionine, proline, and glucose into the cold-TCA-insoluble fraction of *Escherichia coli*. Spherical targets were found for methionine (260 A diameter) and glucose (160 A diameter) incorporation. The target for proline incorporation is a long, thin rod, 22 A in diameter and 2.2 μ long. That the units associated with methionine and glucose correspond closely in size to microsomal particles found in cell debris is therefore evidence for the functional importance of these structures.

The size and shape of the proline-associated incorporation target appear to be those of a nucleic acid unit, although it is not possible to distinguish between RNA and DNA by this method.

The fact that the target determined for glucose incorporation is smaller than that found for the incorporation of the exogenous amino acid methionine indicates that glucose is not directly connected with the binding of incorporated amino acids into bacterial protein.

REFERENCES

1. P. C. Zamecnik and E. B. Keller, *J. Biol. Chem.*, *209*, 337 (1954); J. W. Littlefield, E. B. Keller, J. Gross, and P. C. Zamecnik, *J. Biol. Chem.*, *217*, 111 (1955).

2. F. Hutchinson, H. Morowitz, and E. Kempner, *Science*, *126*, 310 (1957).

3. E. C. Pollard, *Advances in Biol. and Med. Phys.*, *3*, 153 (1953).

4. Conference on Ionizing Radiation and the Cell, L. F. Nims, Chairman, *Ann. N. Y. Acad. Sci.*, *59*, 467–664 (1955).

5. E. C. Pollard, W. R. Guild, F. Hutchinson, and R. B. Setlow, *Progr. in Biophys. and Biophys. Chem.*, *5*, 72 (1955).

6. W. R. Guild and F. DeFilippes, *Biochim. et Biophys. Acta*, *26*, 241 (1957).

7. F. Hutchinson, *Radiation Research*, *7*, 473 (1957).

8. H. K. Schachman, A. B. Pardee, and R. Y. Stanier, *Arch. Biochem. Biophys.*, *38*, 245 (1952).

9. R. B. Roberts, D. B. Cowie, P. H. Abelson, E. T. Bolton, and R. J. Britten, *Studies of Biosynthesis in Escherichia coli*, Carnegie Inst. Wash. Publ. 607, Washington, D. C., 1955.

10. E. C. Pollard, J. Setlow, and E. Watts, *Radiation Research*, *8*, 77 (1958).

11. R. J. Britten, R. B. Roberts, and E. F. French, *Proc. Natl. Acad. Sci. U. S.*, *41*, 863 (1955).

12. G. N. Cohen and H. C. Rickenberg, *Compt. rend.*, *240*, 2086 (1955).

13. Other papers this volume.

14. D. Billen and E. Volkin, *J. Bacteriol.*, *67*, 191 (1954).

17

The Effect of X Rays on the Incorporation
of Phosphorus and Sulfur into *Escherichia coli*

ERNEST POLLARD   JANE KENNEDY

Biophysics Department,[1] Yale University

In the previous paper of this volume an account was given of preliminary studies on the effect of ionizing radiation on the incorporation of amino acids and glucose into a fraction of the bacterial cell that is not soluble in trichloroacetic acid. It is hoped that a continuation of such probing into the synthetic processes in the cell by radiation will give some information on the nature of the processes themselves. Though the subject of keenest interest at the moment is undoubtedly the fate of an individual metabolite, and the way in which it becomes incorporated, it seemed to be important to know something of the way in which radiation affects the uptake of two much more generally utilized elements of the growth medium, phosphate and sulfate. The studies to be described were originally meant simply as a means of gaining general information about the effect of radiation on the cell metabolism, to ensure that no serious discrepancies existed between the findings with one amino acid and the whole metabolic process of the cell. During the studies some results appeared that seem to indicate rather remarkable radiation sensitivities and are, moreover, of interest in themselves. For instance, the ability of the cell to incorporate phosphate is remarkably sensitive to X radiation; the sulfate-incorporation ability is also highly sensitive, though less so; and sulfide incorporation is definitely still less sensitive. The hypothesis that suggests itself is that the phosphorus incorporation is determined by relatively large and sensitive units, and that when these are damaged by radiation there is a proportionally smaller phosphorus uptake. For sulfur uptake the results are in accord with the idea that there is a considerable synthetic chain which presents sensitivity at a num-

[1] Aided by a grant from the United States Public Health Service.

ber of loci. The results are only preliminary, but they do contribute to an emerging picture of cellular processes which is worth some consideration.

Closely related to this work is a series of studies by Billen and Volkin [1], Billen and Lichstein [2], Billen, Stapleton, and Hollaender [3], and Billen [4] on the effect of X rays on several factors in *E. coli*. Their results will be discussed later. Some work by Labaw, Mosley, and Wyckoff [9] is also of interest, though directed at bacteriophage development.

PRINCIPLES OF RADIATION INACTIVATION STUDIES

For these experiments the simplest and most available source of ionizing radiation, X rays, was used. X rays produce ionizations which are distributed along the tracks of secondary electrons, light particles that ionize relatively sparsely. In our arrangements, where 250-kv X rays filtered through 1 mm of aluminum were used, the average secondary-electron energy is in the neighborhood of 50 kv, and so produces ionizations which are generally separated by distances of over 1000 A. Since the electrons scatter readily, the net effect is to produce local energy releases, which average 110 ev each, at random throughout the bacterium. The number per unit volume depends on the dose of radiation, and for the purposes of this paper will be taken as 5×10^{11}/cc/r, which assumes a density of a little over unity for the bacterium.

Many previous studies, quoted in the preceding paper of this volume, have shown that the energy releases can remove biological potency from quite large biological molecules. In proteins it is thought that the reason is the migration of the positive charge left by ionization, along a covalently bonded structure until it reaches a weak point, where chemical action by water or oxygen can cause a destructive chemical change. Then ionization anywhere in the covalently bonded structure is destructive. For nucleic acids the best evidence suggests that either a break in the chain can result, or a cross linking of two chains can take place, both drastic events. In any event, the philosophy of these experiments is to estimate the chance of complete escape from any ionization at all, arguing that the chance of being ionized and escaping any effect is statistically too low to be worth considering. Such estimates are, of course, tentative to some degree. Nevertheless, the sum of 10 years' work in our laboratory, together with the findings of many others, renders them plausible.

The structure that is being bombarded by these random energy releases is shown in the section electron micrograph in figure 1. The section is of two *Escherichia coli* bacteria, one of which has passed into a rather filamentous form, and the other of which is normal. The sectioning and microscopy are entirely due to L. Caro of our laboratory, and the illustration is presented by his permission. It shows clearly the presence of an inner region, almost certainly the locale of the DNA, as has been shown by Caro, Van Tubergen, and Forro [5], and an outer region which contains microsomal particles, or "ribosomes," and which is presumed to be the region of protein synthesis. Figure 2

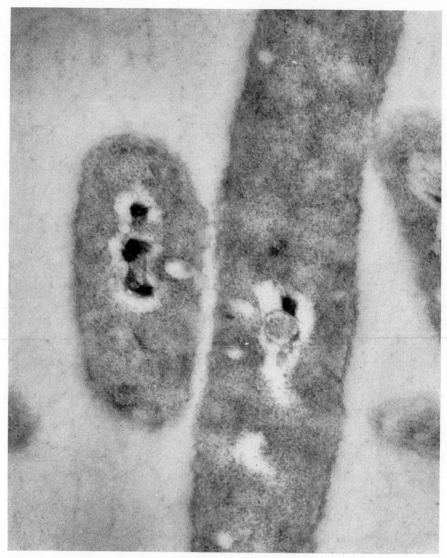

Fig. 1. An electron micrograph of a thin section of *E. coli,* taken by L. Caro. The ribosome granules can be seen in the body of the cell. The inner region, presumed to contain DNA, can be seen, and the structure of the cell wall is also apparent.

is a schematic drawing of the escape process, in which one of the ribosomes is indicated as present in a region 1000 A square and 100 A deep, with the appropriate energy releases accompanying it. On the left is the effect produced by 10,000 r, and the microsomal particle is shown to scale with the single ionization which is to be expected accompanying it. According to the studies of Hutchinson [6], in a cell containing the normal proportion of water there can

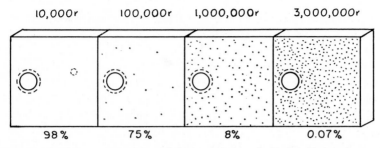

Fig. 2. A schematic representation of the statistical analysis of radiation damage. It is supposed that to escape damage a microsomal particle must escape an ionization in its structure, or even the diffusion of an active agent from ionization to its structure. The probability of escape can be seen to be clearly dependent on the particle size and the amount of ionization.

be a migration by diffusion of the energy release to the extent of 30 A. This little spread of energy has been indicated by a dotted line around the ionization. It can be seen that the chance of escape at 10,000 r is very good, the calculated figure being 98 per cent. In the second region the microsomal particle has been given an increase of 30 A in radius to allow for the possibility of migration of energy, and now each ionization has to be considered as a single dot. The chance of escape is now less but still high; it is estimated at 75 per cent. With 1,000,000 r it is only 8 per cent, and with 3,000,000 r the chance of escape is very remote indeed, and it is expressed by the unlikely figure of 0.07 per cent.

The experimental method, therefore, is to expose bacterial cultures held in a static condition by being chilled to 4° C to X rays, to permit them to warm up, and then to add labeled phosphate or sulfate to them and observe the uptake of radioactivity as compared with the uptake of the unirradiated preparation. The ratio of the two is then compared with the chance of escape, and deductions regarding the size of the particle are made from this probability.

EXPERIMENTAL METHOD

The experiments with phosphate are complicated by the fact that very commonly phosphate buffer is used in minimal media. This means that a large excess of cold phosphate is present, rendering uptake somewhat difficult. Accordingly the procedure we evolved was to grow the bacteria overnight in the C minimal medium as described by Roberts, Abelson, Bolton, Britten, and Cowie [7] and then transfer for a 90-minute growth period to Tris buffered medium containing 80 mg of phosphate/l. The 90 minutes permitted the bacteria to establish themselves satisfactorily in the new medium; they were then chilled and irradiated with a 250-kv X-ray machine at approximately 3000 r/minute. Subsequent to irradiation both the control and the irradiated sample were warmed in a 37° bath and an appropriate number of counts of radioactive phosphate was added to each one. The bacteria were sampled at

different intervals of time by means of a small syringe and filtered through an
S and S filter. The filters, after being stored to dry, were counted in the
ordinary way.

For sulfate the same procedure was adopted because it was thought worth
while to compare phosphate and sulfate uptake under similar conditions. For
the uptake of sulfides we encountered considerable difficulty, as was pointed
out by Cowie, in that the sulfide very readily formed sulfate and does not stay
in its original form. We overcame this to some extent, though not always consistently, by having an excess of cold sulfide present and by working as rapidly
as was consistent with the experiment. When fresh radioactive sulfide and
fresh sodium sulfide were used the data indicated a very clear difference from
those obtained with sulfate and could also be made to give consistent results
though not quite to the same degree as sulfate uptake.

EXPERIMENTAL RESULTS

The form of an uptake curve for phosphate is shown in figure 3. The experiments differ from those of the previous paper in that there is no limitation
in the amount of tracer and so the bacteria can continue to incorporate phosphorus throughout a whole period of 2 hours. It can be seen that for the control and the slightly irradiated points there is an exponential uptake of P^{32} but
that at the higher doses the uptake becomes linear. By comparing the early
slopes of the lines a survival ratio can be obtained which can then be plotted

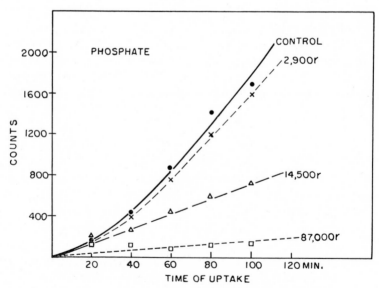

Fig. 3. The results of one individual experiment on phosphate uptake. The control and
least-irradiated cultures show exponential uptake; the more heavily irradiated cultures show
reduced linear uptake.

against the dose. The change from logarithmic to linear increase is significant and probably means, as pointed out by Cohen [8], that some unit is being formed in the irradiated cell which is not suitable for further growth. The cell is then continuing to operate on its existing material and not making fresh.

With radioactive sulfate the curves shown in figure 4 were obtained. These are the results of a single run, and they are very similar to the uptake curve for phosphate except that the sensitivity to ionizing radiation is not quite so great. In the course of study we noticed that the initial part of the curve did not seem to be as greatly affected by ionizing radiation as later stages, and accordingly a deliberate attempt to study this was made, with the results shown in figure 5. Much higher doses were employed, and it is apparent that the effect of quite high doses on sulfate uptake is to cause a breaking away from an initial line which occurs progressively earlier and earlier in the uptake process. The final slope of the uptake is diminished as found previously, but the breaking-away point seems to come later and later with lower and lower dose.

This again seems to indicate that the effect of radiation is on some mechanism in the cell that prevents future development of means for further growth.

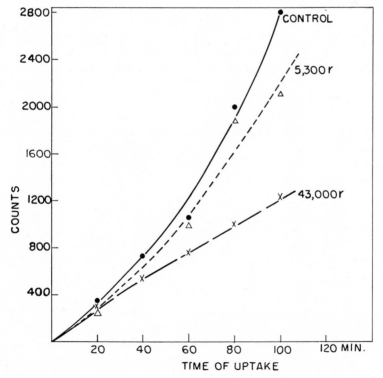

Fig. 4. The results of one uptake experiment on sulfate. For low irradiations the exponential character remains, but at higher doses the uptake becomes linear. The uptake is less sensitive than that of PO_4.

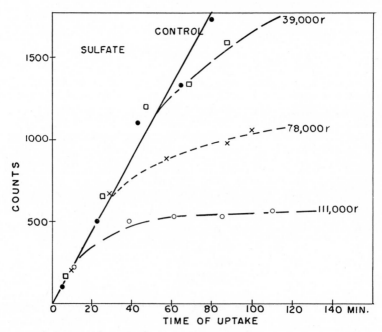

Fig. 5. The initial uptake of sulfate at higher doses. For 10 minutes, even at a dose of 111,000 r, the uptake is normal. Thereafter, the rate of uptake breaks away from normal, at earlier times for higher doses. The implication is that some synthesis can go on with the original synthetic apparatus but that adequate provision for future synthesis is not made in irradiated cells.

The initial processes in the cell seem to be capable of continuing, but they run out and the damage to the cell then becomes apparent.

The incorporation of sulfide was studied in much the same way. The results again look very similar to those found for sulfate except that still higher doses were necessary to produce an effect, and also there was some indication that the inactivation instead of being linear was curved. This might mean that more than one process is involved in sulfide uptake.

By way of check experiments, the number of colonies produced after irradiation was also studied and the effect of radiation on the optical density was measured. The optical density is that after a standard period of growth, usually about 80 minutes.

The results of all these experiments can be seen in figure 6, where curves for per cent remaining versus radiation dose in roentgens are plotted. It can be seen that by far the most sensitive factor is the formation of colonies and that this is followed, in order, by phosphate and sulfate uptake, optical density, and sulfide uptake. Lastly, the effect on the methionine uptake is very small indeed and can hardly be plotted on the graph. Analyzed in terms of the probability of escape as mentioned earlier, the data are presented in table 1.

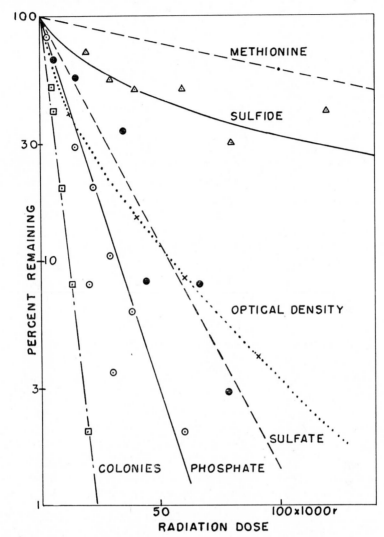

Fig. 6. Logarithmic dose response plots for colony counts, optical density, and phosphate, sulfate, sulfide, and methionine uptakes. The relative sensitivities can be analyzed in terms of sensitive volumes, which are given in table 1.

The most surprising result is the great sensitivity of phosphorus uptake. It is difficult to see how the relatively simple processes involving phosphate can be involved with such large target units. A repeat of the uptake, using C minimal medium, has been made, with results still indicating a great sensitivity, though perhaps not as great as in Tris. We are at a loss to explain the finding, and rather than speculate about the control of phosphorus uptake by large units of DNA we prefer to continue studies aimed at finding the nature of the damaged products. It should be pointed out that, with all three tracers, phosphate,

TABLE 1

Process	37% Dose, r	Sensitive Volume, cc	Fraction of Cell
Colony formation	5,000	4×10^{-16}	2.7×10^{-4}
Optical density			
Initial slope	8,500	2.4×10^{-16}	1.5×10^{-4}
Final slope	43,000	4.7×10^{-17}	3×10^{-5}
Phosphate uptake	14,000	1.4×10^{-16}	9×10^{-5}
Sulfate uptake	23,000	8.7×10^{-17}	6×10^{-5}
Sulfide uptake	40,000	5×10^{-17}	3×10^{-5}
Methionine uptake	200,000	10^{-17}	6.5×10^{-6}

sulfate, and sulfide, the initial uptake is unaltered. This finding was reported previously by Billen and his associates [1, 2, 3, 4], and we confirm it.

For the sulfate and sulfide data a simple explanation can be advanced. It is best seen diagrammatically as in figure 7. We suppose that the synthesis of protein is determined by the presence of intact units of the size stated in the previous paper for methionine. However, the protein made can be essential for the enzymatic reduction of sulfate or combination of reduced sulfur with other elements to form intermediates, finally ending in methionine, cysteine, or glutathione. Each enzyme is a protein and probably requires methionine or cysteine, i.e., sulfur in the right form. The entire uptake of sulfur is thus sensitive in three ways: first as final incorporation into protein, second as requiring the availability of a suitable enzyme for a needed process, third in terms of the synthesis of such enzymes. The sensitivity of methionine incorporation then requires only the functioning of one ribosome. Sulfate will not be incorporated, however, if enzymes are inactivated (experience shows this inactivation to be relatively difficult, as each enzyme molecule is small), or if enzyme synthesis is stopped, or if protein synthesis is stopped. Thus a much larger inactivation volume for sulfate uptake can be predicted. From the ratio of the inactivation volume for sulfate uptake, after the initial stage is over, to that for methionine uptake, the number of steps involved can be estimated. From table 1 the steps from sulfate to methionine are 8.7, and from sulfide to methionine 5. The process is shown schematically in figure 7. We make no claim for correct intermediary biochemistry. If the explanation we propose is right it could be checked against known intermediary processes by means of competition techniques. This check is planned for future work.

One question naturally asked concerns any change in the fractions in the cell after irradiation. We studied the four fractions: alcohol-soluble, cold-TCA-soluble, hot-TCA-soluble, and residue. The results are shown in table 2. We found the relative proportion of S^{35} in the hot-TCA-soluble and residue fractions to depend somewhat on the time and temperature of exposure to hot TCA, and we do not regard the variations in the hot-TCA fraction as significant. Possibly the fall in the alcohol-soluble fraction after heavy irradiation in sulfate

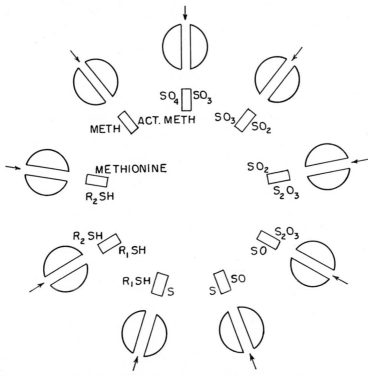

Fig. 7. A schematic diagram to indicate the reason for the high sensitivity of sulfate uptake. A series of reduction and combination steps, requiring enzymes (indicated as rectangles), has to be complete before the activated amino acid can be incorporated. Each enzyme is made by a microsomal particle vulnerable to radiation. Hence the sensitivity for a nine-step process is nine times higher than for a single step.

medium is a real effect. Otherwise the major conclusion is that no change in the broad distribution is observed.

That the initial uptake is unchanged, but reduced uptake occurs sooner for more heavily irradiated cells, argues that a considerable amount of incorporation can go with the damaged synthetic apparatus, but that an unbalance occurs as the cell develops. If the damaged ribosomes were making enzymati-

TABLE 2. Cell Fractionation under Various Conditions

Fraction	Unirradiated Sulfide	50 kr Sulfide	Unirradiated Sulfate	300,000 r Sulfate
Alcohol-soluble (lipids, protein)	20	21	22	12
Cold-TCA-soluble (transient intermediates, glutathione)	5	4	5.5	8
Hot-TCA-soluble (nucleic acid hydrolysates)	18	8	6	12
Residue (protein)	60	69	67	69

cally impotent protein, such would be the case. The linear rather than exponential uptake in damaged cells tends to argue in favor of this hypothesis. We intend to study specific cell fractions as a check.

ACKNOWLEDGMENTS

We wish to thank Stuart Hauser for assistance in the later stages, particularly for the data for figure 5. Discussions with Ellis Kempner have been most useful.

SUMMARY

The uptake of P^{32} phosphate and S^{35} sulfate and sulfide by *E. coli* as influenced by X rays has been studied. The initial uptake is not greatly changed by doses up to 100,000 r, but the rate of uptake is radically changed at later times. Expressing the ratio of the final rate of uptake to that of unirradiated controls in terms of dose we find a logarithmic relation. Analysis in terms of a sensitive volume gives large sensitivities as follows:

Colony formation (for comparison)	4×10^{-16} cc
PO_4 uptake	1.4×10^{-16}
SO_4 uptake	9.5×10^{-17}
S uptake	5×10^{-17}
Methionine uptake (for comparison)	10^{-17}

The surprisingly large sensitivity for phosphate may mean that intact DNA controls phosphorus uptake. The figures for sulfate, sulfide, and methionine can be explained in terms of a synthetic chain of microsomal particles involving nine steps from SO_4 to protein and five from sulfide to protein.

REFERENCES

1. D. Billen and E. Volkin, Effect of X-rays on the macromolecular organization of *E. coli* B/r, *J. Bacteriol., 67,* 191–197 (1954).

2. D. Billen and H. C. Lichstein, Effect of X-radiation on the adaptive formation of formic hydrogenlyase, *J. Bacteriol., 63,* 553–555 (1952).

3. D. Billen, G. E. Stapleton, and A. Hollaender, The effect of X-radiation on the respiration of *E. coli, J. Bacteriol., 65,* 131 (1953).

4. D. Billen, Modification of the release of cellular constituents by irradiated *E. coli, Arch. Biochem. Biophys., 67,* 333–340 (1957).

5. L. Caro, R. T. Van Tubergen, and F. Forro, Jr., Radioautography of sectioned bacteria, *Biophysical Society Program Abstract R 12,* 1958.

6. F. Hutchinson, The distance that a radical formed by ionizing radiation can diffuse in a yeast cell, *Radiation Research, 7,* 473–483 (1957).

7. R. B. Roberts, P. H. Abelson, D. B. Cowie, E. T. Bolton, and R. J. Britten, *Studies of Biosynthesis in Escherichia coli,* Carnegie Inst. Wash. Publ. 607, Washington, D. C., 1955.

8. G. N. Cohen, Synthèse de protéines anormales chez *Escherichia coli* K-12 cultivé en présence de L-valine, *Ann. inst. Pasteur, 94,* 15–30 (1958).

9. L. W. Labaw, V. M. Mosley, and R. W. Wyckoff, Development of bacteriophage in x-ray inactivated bacteria, *J. Bacteriol., 65,* 330–336 (1953).

18

Statistical Relations in the Amino Acid Order of *Escherichia coli* Protein[1]

HAROLD J. MOROWITZ

Biophysics Department, Yale University

Since proteins consist largely of chains of amino acids, a formal analogy is suggested between protein structure and written language, which consists of chains of letters. The analogy breaks down when we come to consider function. For the function (meaning) of language is completely determined by the sequence of letters, whereas the function of proteins depends on the secondary structure (coiling) was well as on the sequence. (In poetry, secondary structure is extremely important.)

One characteristic of both proteins and language is the nonrandom frequency of occurrence of letters. Thus if we examine a long passage written in English we get a rank frequency distribution represented by figure 1, which also shows the rank frequency distribution of amino acids in *Escherichia coli* protein. Further examination of language reveals certain high-frequency pairs, triplets, and higher groupings of letters [1, 2].

A further feature shows up on inspection of amino acid composition of protein. The nonrandom distribution of amino acids that is apparent in over-all collections of proteins arises from a similar nonrandomness in individual proteins. There are notable exceptions to these relations, however, particularly in structural proteins like silk and collagen.

A further question suggests itself. In proteins, are there pairs, triplets, and higher amino acid sequences that occur with unexpectedly high or low frequencies? That is, are there laws, similar to the laws of language, governing the ordering of amino acids in peptide chains? These statistical relations could be the result of thermodynamic stability, of evolutionary selection, or of the

[1] This research aided by a grant from the United States Public Health Service.

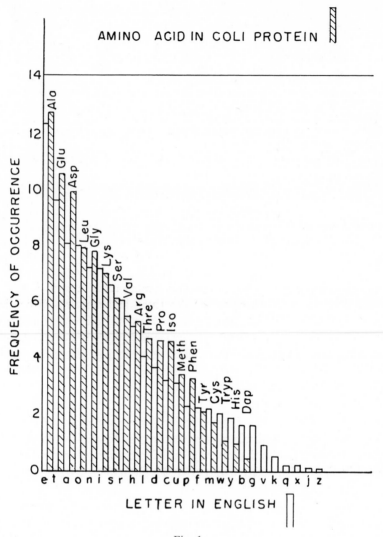

Fig. 1.

mode of synthesis of protein. Regardless of their cause, knowledge of them would place severe restrictions on our theories of synthetic cellular processes.

In recent years a number of workers have tried to elucidate relations among amino acids by examining experimentally available sequences and frequencies [3]. These attempts have been thwarted by some serious difficulties. The known sequences are selected by the small size and ease of purification of the proteins involved. The proteins are thus often unrelated as to source or function. The failure, in this limited range, to find constraints should therefore not be taken as the final word on the problem.

An alternative method of investigating the ordering relations is to give up dealing with pure proteins and examine mixtures of related proteins in an effort to elucidate statistical relations. Thus we may inquire into the frequency distribution of N-terminal amino acids, C-terminal amino acids, amino acids made N terminal by tryptic digestion, or any other experimentally available cut. We may look at the entire collection of proteins from a single cell type, or any subgrouping of proteins definable by some experimental procedure. It must be kept in mind that we are seeking general laws for given collections of proteins.

The experimental procedures are derivable from the techniques of sequence analysis [4]. In particular, use is made of the fluorodinitrobenzene reaction and the Edman degradation [5]. The application of these techniques must be modified, as we are dealing with a collection of proteins rather than a single protein.

Since detailed experimental protocols are being published elsewhere, we shall only outline the method here [6]. *E. coli* cells are grown on a defined medium and randomly labeled with a single radioactive amino acid (leucine) or in the case of sulfur 35 label they are randomly labeled in three amino acids, cysteine, cystine, and methionine. The cells are then washed, and extracted with ethanol, ether, and hot trichloroacetic acid. The residual material containing most of the cell protein and little else is subjected to oxidation with performic acid. One portion of this material is subjected to fluorodinitrobenzene end group analysis or conversion to the phenylthiohydantoin derivatives; a second portion is digested to completion with trypsin and then subjected to the same end group analysis. Quantitative end group analysis is carried out by counting the spots on paper chromatograms that result from N-terminal amino acids and interior amino acids.

We thus determine the frequency of occurrence of cysteine (including cystine), methionine, and leucine in their positions, N terminal and following the tryptic cut (which has a high degree of specificity for the carboxyl end of arginine and lysine). The results of these experiments are shown in table 1.

TABLE 1

Amino Acid	Percentage of Amino Acid in N-Terminal Positions	Percentage of Amino Acid following Tryptic Cut
Methionine	3.6	13.4
Cystine and cysteine	1.5	8.3
Leucine	Less than 0.2	6–9

To interpret these results, let us first consider what results would have been obtained if there were no ordering rules. That is, suppose that each protein sequence was completely independent and any ordering was equally probable. If there were a large number of different protein species, on a statistical basis the amino acids would be expected to be randomly ordered. On the basis of average chain length as calculated from Van Slyke amino nitrogen determinations any amino acid should be N terminal 1.5 per cent of the time and should follow the tryptic cut about 14 per cent of the time.

Failure to observe these ratios indicates one of two situations: either there are statistical rules of sequence, or a small number of protein species contributes a large fraction of the total protein mass. Recent results reported on the column separation of *E. coli* proteins [7] indicate that the protein mass is distributed with reasonable uniformity among a large number of proteins or protein groups. Thus, the results presented in table 1 suggest that statistical rules of sequence are operative in specifying *E. coli* proteins.

REFERENCES

1. H. F. Gaines, *Cryptanalysis,* Dover Publications, Inc., 1956.

2. R. B. Roberts et al., *Studies of Biosynthesis in Escherichia coli,* Carnegie Inst. Wash. Publ. 607, Washington, D. C., 1955.

3. G. Gamow et al., *Advances in Biol. and Med. Phys., 4,* 23 (1956).

4. C. B. Anfinsen and R. R. Redfield, *Advances in Protein Chem., 11,* 1 (1956).

5. Fraenkel-Conrat et al., *Methods of Biochem. Anal., 2,* 399 (1955).

6. H. J. Morowitz and M. Spaulding, *Biochim. et Biophys. Acta,* in press.

7. Work reported in this volume by workers at Carnegie Institution of Washington, Department of Terrestrial Magnetism.

19

The Formation of Protomorphs

FRANK T. McCLURE [1]   RICHARD B. ROBERTS

Department of Terrestrial Magnetism
Carnegie Institution of Washington

Disrupted cells of *Escherichia coli* were suspended in a number of different solutions to find which ones were suitable for making stable preparations of ribosomes. Among those tested were some containing manganese and magnesium, because these ions had been found essential for incorporation of amino acids by cell-free systems [1, 2]. After standing for several hours these solutions became turbid and finally gave a white precipitate of unusual appearance.

Examination of these solutions in the phase contrast microscope showed that the turbidity was caused almost entirely by the presence of large numbers of nearly spherical, highly refractile particles with diameters of 1 to 5 microns (figs. 1 and 2).

The appearance of these cell-like particles in a solution that originally contained nothing visible in the microscope was quite surprising. The formation of large, stable aggregates with distinct boundaries from a fluid containing macromolecules in a homogeneous suspension seemed to illustrate a process which perhaps was important in the origin of life. Accordingly, we proceeded to investigate some of their properties. It was soon found that the particles contained protein, nucleic acid, and lipid in proportions typical of biological materials. Because they are formed from protoplasm and have distinctive shape we refer to them as "protomorphs" to distinguish them from other particles or structures that exist in the living cell.

The usual procedure for preparation of protomorphs is as follows: Harvest 10 g wet weight of *Escherichia coli* cells growing in synthetic medium "C" [3]. Wash twice with tris(hydroxymethyl)aminomethane-succinate buffer, 0.01 M,

---

[1] Present address: Johns Hopkins University, Applied Physics Laboratory, 8121 Georgia Avenue, Silver Spring, Maryland.

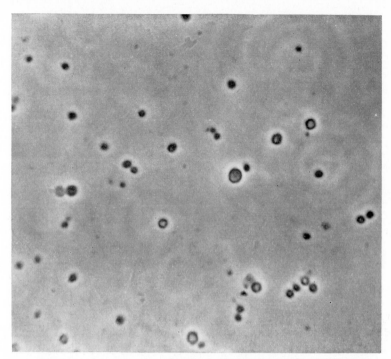

Fig. 1. Protomorphs in the solution from which they form.

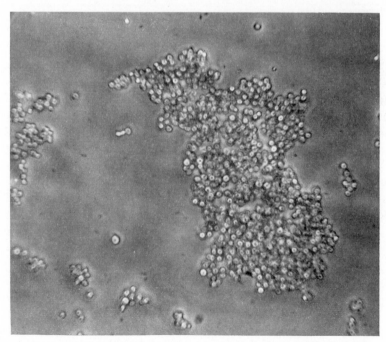

Fig. 2. Aggregated protomorphs scraped off glass surface. Phase contrast photomicrographs taken by W. R. Duryee.

*p*H 7.6 (TS). Suspend with 10 ml TS, and break the cells by forcing the suspension through an orifice at 10,000 psi with a flow rate of roughly 2 ml/min. Add TS to bring the total volume to 50 ml, and centrifuge 15 minutes at 40,000*g*. Discard the precipitate, which contains unbroken cells and large fragments of cell walls. Centrifuge again at 105,000*g* for 15 minutes, and discard the precipitate, which contains smaller fragments of cell walls and a small proportion of the ribosomes. Dilute the supernatant fluid with TS to 100 ml, and add $MgCl_2$ and $MnCl_2$ to make it 0.005 M in each. In 5 to 48 hours the solution will show turbidity because of protomorph formation. The entire procedure is carried out at 0° to 5° C.

The yield of this procedure is variable, as is the time required for formation of the protomorphs. Some of the sources of variability have been identified; others remain unknown.

The addition of manganese is essential. No protomorphs were formed when Mn^{++} was omitted even though adequate Mg^{++} was present. Higher concentrations of Mn^{++} (0.01 M to 0.5 M) caused the formation of a precipitate of particles of irregular shape and widely variable size. No attempt was made to find other cations that might substitute for the Mn^{++}. The Mg^{++} was not essential but seemed to increase the yield. No difference was noted whether the magnesium was added before or after the cells were broken; thus there would appear to be no difference to protomorph formation whether the ribosomes were in the 80 S form or not (see paper 3 of this volume).

No protomorphs were formed when the *p*H of the solution was outside the limits 7 to 8; a *p*H of 7.5 seemed to be optimum.

The concentration of orthophosphate affects the yield. When the cells are carefully washed in TS before breaking, the phosphate of the growth medium is removed and phosphate must be added to give a concentration of 10^{-3} M. If higher quantities of phosphate are added the particles become less refractile in appearance and are dark, rough, and "hairy." At still higher concentrations of phosphate, precipitates are formed in manganese solutions lacking cellular material. Although these inorganic precipitates have only a slight resemblance to the protomorphs, it is possible that the inorganic material provides a framework on which the organic material deposits.

The concentration of the cellular material is important. When the usual procedure was followed a twofold dilution of the cell extract prevented the formation of protomorphs. The presence of cell-wall material was not important to the yield; the yield was the same whether or not the centrifugation steps to remove cell walls and unbroken cells were omitted. When the wall material was present the protomorphs appeared less smooth, as if irregular fragments of wall had been incorporated.

The constituent responsible for the sensitivity to the concentration is probably deoxyribonucleic acid (DNA). The addition of DNAase invariably prevents the formation of protomorphs. The pressure cell routinely used to disrupt the cells also degrades DNA, as preparations of DNA lose their viscosity on being forced through the orifice of the pressure cell. Cell juices prepared with the pressure cell do not show the peak characteristic of DNA in their sedimentation diagram [4]. It is these preparations (made with the pressure cell) that will not give protomorphs when diluted. In contrast, preparations made by grinding the cells with alumina or by lysozyme treatment followed by osmotic shock (methods which preserve DNA) do yield protomorphs even at one-tenth the usual concentration. Finally, the addition of DNA to dilute pressure-cell preparations restores the yield. It seems quite likely that variations in the pressure and in the conditions at the orifice during the disruption of the cells affect the quantity of intact DNA remaining and thereby influence the yield in an erratic way.

The formation of protomorphs was photographed by Drs. B. Hoyer and N. Kramis, of the Rocky Mountain Laboratory, U. S. Public Health Service. Their time-lapse photomicrography shows that the growth of an individual protomorph from its first appearance to full size requires only a few minutes after a much longer induction period. There may well be a slow process of nucleation followed by a rapid process of growth. Neither fission nor fusion played any part in the growth process.

Once formed, the protomorphs are stable. Unlike simple coacervate particles which exist only in a narrow pH range and have a strong tendency to fuse or to dissolve, protomorphs can be handled like bacteria or yeast. There is no difficulty in centrifuging the photomorphs into a pellet ($1000g$) and resuspending in fresh media. They are quite stable in a number of ordinary media, and persist for weeks even though overgrown by bacterial contamination. They are not dissolved by short exposures to ammonia ($1\ M$), 5 per cent trichloroacetic acid (TCA), ethanol, or ether. They are dissolved in $0.01\ M$ ethylenediaminetetraacetic acid to give a clear solution.

On standing, glass vessels containing protomorph suspensions develop a white film over the surface. Microscopic examination of the material scraped from the glass indicates that the protomorphs have formed a moderately well packed monolayer on the surface (fig. 2).

The organic components of the particles had roughly the proportions found in living tissues. They contain ultraviolet-absorbing material which hydrolyzes to yield the bases expected from ribonucleic acid. In addition the diphenylamine test [5] indicates that a small part (10 per cent) of the ultraviolet absorption is due to DNA. The ratio of nucleic acid to protein (measured by the Folin reaction [6]) is 1/6 as compared to 1/4 in the bacterial juice. Paper chromatography shows the presence of lipid material.

Incorporation experiments were carried out with thoroughly washed preparations of protomorphs. Radioactive phosphate was incorporated at a constant, high rate for several hours. This process was not studied in any detail because all the radioactivity so incorporated could be extracted with cold TCA and there was no evidence of incorporation into macromolecules.

The incorporation of radioactive amino acids was of more interest. The results were erratic from one preparation to another, and the incorporation rate was only 1/1000 that of intact cells at the highest. Accordingly contamination by intact cells was a constant worry. The number of intact cells was estimated both by plate counts and by microscopic examination. The uptake observed was as much as 100 times that which could be attributed to the contaminants.

There were also several qualitative features which distinguish the behavior of the protomorph preparation from that of intact cells. In the first place, the incorporation doubled if ATP was added or if the concentration of the amino acid mixture was doubled. These variations have little effect on incorporation by whole cells. Secondly, the distribution of incorporated radioactivity among the fractions soluble in cold TCA, alcohol, ether, and hot TCA was different from that obtained with whole cells [3]. Finally, the hot-TCA-insoluble material after hydrolysis yielded a pattern of radioactive amino acids different from the mixture supplied and different from what would be incorporated by whole cells.

Accordingly we believe that the observed incorporation was in fact real, though not reproducible from day to day. Since these experiments were done we have learned of the activity of the cell-wall fraction in protein synthesis [7, 8]. In retrospect it seems quite likely that the variability in the synthetic capacity of the protomorphs may have been due to a variability in their content of cell-wall fragments.

These protomorphs are of course very different from the ribosomes which are the subject of this symposium, but there may be a relationship between them. It is a common belief that the bacterial cell is not a homogeneous mixture of its various components; on the contrary, various lines of evidence indicate that it has a high degree of organization. Organization in turn implies the action of forces between the various constituents such as DNA, RNA, protein, and ribosomes. It is possible that the aggregation of these cellular constituents into protomorphs may be another manifestation of the same forces which maintain organization in the living cell and may furnish a material in which the forces are more amenable to study. If so, the protomorphs may eventually contribute to our knowledge of how the ribosomes are organized within the cell.

REFERENCES

1. S. Spiegelman, *A Symposium on the Chemical Basis of Heredity*, p. 232, Johns Hopkins Press, 1957.

2. B. Nisman, personal communication, 1957.

3. R. B. Roberts, P. H. Abelson, D. B. Cowie, E. T. Bolton, and R. J. Britten, *Studies of Biosynthesis in Escherichia coli*, Carnegie Inst. Wash. Publ. 607, 1955.

4. E. T. Bolton, B. H. Hoyer, and D. B. Ritter, paper 3 of this volume.

5. Z. Dische, *The Nucleic Acids*, vol. I, chapter 9, Academic Press, New York, 1955.

6. O. H. Lowry, N. J. Rosebrough, A. L. Farr, and R. J. Randall, *J. Biol. Chem., 193*, 265 (1951).

7. V. R. Srinivasan and S. Spiegelman, *Bacteriol. Proc., 58*, 101 (1958).

8. S. Ochoa, Spring Meeting, National Academy of Sciences, 1958.

20

Structure of Microsomal Nucleoprotein
Particles from Pea Seedlings[1]

PAUL O. P. TS'O

Division of Biology, California Institute of Technology

Microsomal nucleoprotein particles from pea seedlings have been isolated and characterized in our laboratories [1]. These particles have an RNA/protein ratio of 4/6 and a molecular weight of 4 to 4.5×10^6, and they appear in the electron microscope as oblate spheroids (fig. 1). The microsomal nucleoprotein particles of pea seedlings thus seem to be similar to those of yeast [2], liver [3], and perhaps also to those of bacteria as reported in this meeting.

The problem of the structure of the particles can be approached from at least three lines of inquiry. (1) How are the smaller units of nucleoprotein put together in the 80 S particles? (2) How are the RNA and protein put together in the nucleoprotein? (3) If protein synthesis takes place in the particle, what is the structural relation of the newly synthesized protein to the nucleoprotein that constitutes the particle? The present paper is principally concerned with the first of these questions.

Two salient features of the approach and of the interpretation should first be noted. Experimentally, every precaution has been taken to assure that the dissociation agents employed do not exert hydrolytic action on covalent bonds. In interpreting the results of dissociation studies, it is assumed that all particles in the preparation have similar gross structure. The simple ultracentrifugal patterns of the dissociated particles, and the reversibility of certain dissociating processes, seem to support this assumption. It is entirely conceivable, however, that though in general features the subunits of all the particles may be very similar, the cohesive strength with which they stick together inside the particle

[1] This work was supported in part by grants Nos. Rg-3977 and Rg-5143 from the National Institutes of Health, United States Public Health Service.

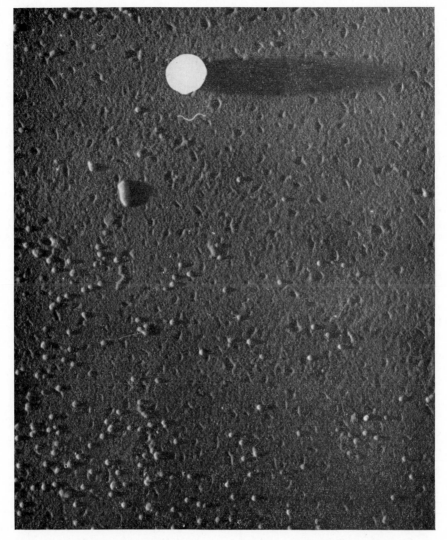

Fig. 1. Electron micrograph of a freeze-dry preparation of microsomal particles from pea seedlings. Magnification 41,000×; thorium shadowed with an angle of 6.5:1.

may vary during the different phases of cell growth and differentiation. Preliminary information suggesting that this is so has been reported in this meeting: information concerning rapidly growing cells, such as those of yeast and bacteria. Eventually, then, studies of structure of particles in the steady state will evolve into studies of structure of particles through a life cycle.

Processes or agents that remove or substitute divalent ions from the particles promote dissociation of the particles. For instance, in a 0.8 per cent particle solution, in pH 6.5, 0.025 μ, phosphate buffer, there is only 6 per cent dissociation of 80 S particles into 60 S and 40 S units. In pH 7.5, 0.05 μ, buffer, there is 50 per cent dissociation, and in pH 8.5 buffer, there is over 80 per cent dissociation (fig. 2a, b, c). Substantially, all the subunits in pH 7.5, 0.05 μ, phosphate buffer can be returned to the form of 80 S particles either by addition of magnesium $(5 \times 10^{-4}\,M)$ or by titration of the pH back to pH 6.5 (fig. 2d, e). Thus, the dissociation of 80 S particles to 60 S and 40 S units is a reversible one. Increase in pH or concentration of phosphate buffer promotes the dissociation by taking magnesium away from the particles. This interpretation is

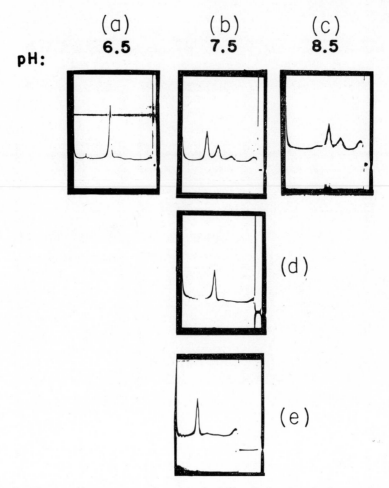

Fig. 2. Ultracentrifuge patterns of particles in 0.05 μ K-phosphate buffer as affected by pH. Speed 35,600 rpm. (a) In pH 6.5 buffer at 0° C for 13 hours. (b) In pH 7.5 buffer at 0° C for 16 hours. (c) In pH 8.5 buffer at 0° C for 1½ hours. (d) Solution in pH 7.5, 0° C for 2 hours, back-titrated with phosphoric acid to pH 6.5, stored at 0° C for 3 hours. (e) Solution in pH 7.5, 0° C for 1½ hours. MgCl₂ added to final concentration of $5 \times 10^{-4}\,M$, stored at 0°C for 3 hours.

further substantiated by experiments on dialysis of the particles. When a particle preparation is dialyzed against a buffer in which it is stable, dissociation to 60 S and 40 S units occurs (fig. 3*a*, *d*). This dissociation is caused by removal by dialysis of essential cofactor(s), since it can be prevented or reversed by dialyzing the particles against the deproteinized supernatant (fig. 3*b*, *e*). The cofactor is present in the supernatant of the extract from which the particles were originally isolated; it is completely heat stable and not absorbed on charcoal; finally, its protective and dissociation-reversing properties have been duplicated by magnesium chloride, 5×10^{-4} *M* (fig. 3*c*, *f*). Calcium chloride

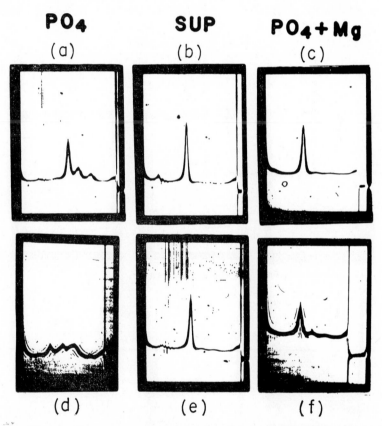

Fig. 3. Ultracentrifuge patterns of particles after dialysis. Speed 36,500 rpm. (*a*) Dialysis against 0.025 *μ* K-PO$_4$, *p*H 6.5, 2–4° C, for 13 hours. (*b*) Supernatant, plus 0.025 *μ* K-PO$_4$, *p*H 6.5, 2–4° C, for 14 hours. (*c*) 0.025 *μ* K-PO$_4$, *p*H 6.5, 5×10^{-4} *M* MgCl$_2$, 2–4° C, for 19 hours. (*d*) 0.025 *μ* K-PO$_4$, *p*H 6.5, 2–4° C, for 24 hours. (*e*) Solution first dialyzed in phosphate buffer to produce solution of (*a*), and the solution of (*a*) redialyzed against supernatant with 0.025 *μ* K-PO$_4$, *p*H 6.5, 2–4° C, 14 hours. (*f*) Solution first dialyzed in phosphate buffer to produce a solution similar to (*a*), and the solution of 75, 60, and 40 S particles redialyzed against 0.025 *μ* K-PO$_4$, *p*H 6.5, with 5×10^{-4} *M* MgCl$_2$, 2–4° C, for 14 hours.

at the same concentration has also been found to have protective properties. Similar results have been obtained for yeast particles [4].

The dissociation of particles to smaller subunits is a relatively rapid process. Thus, essentially the same proportions between 80, 60, and 40 S components are obtained in runs on materials incubated at 0° C in phosphate buffer, pH 7.5, 0.05 μ, for 2 minutes or for 16 hours. No evidence was found in these experiments to suggest that the 60 and 40 S components are formed by aggregation of smaller products.

In concentrated potassium chloride solution (0.35 to 0.7 M), the particles also dissociate into 60 and 40 S (fig. 4b, e) subunits, and this process too is substantially reversible (fig. 4b, c). Addition of magnesium chloride (0.015 to

KCl 0.7M

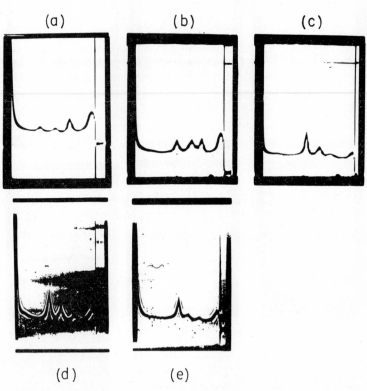

Fig. 4. Ultracentrifuge patterns of particles in KCl solutions. (a) In 0.7 M KCl, 24° C, for 30 minutes. Rotor speed 35,600 rpm. (b) In 0.7 M KCl, 0° C, for 1 hour. Centrifuged at 7° C. Rotor speed 42,040 rpm. (c) Solution of (b) dialyzed in 0.025 μ K-PO$_4$, pH 6.5, MgCl$_2$1 × 10^{-3} M, 2–4° C, for 14 hours. Centrifuged at 6.8° C. Rotor speed 42,040 rpm. (d) In 0.7 M KCl with 0.015 M MgCl$_2$, 0° C, for 1 hour. Rotor speed 35,600 rpm. (e) In 0.35 M KCl, 0° C, for 1 hour. Rotor speed 35,600 rpm.

0.1 *M*) partly suppresses but does not completely eliminate the dissociation (fig. 4*d*). The effects of potassium chloride are, therefore, probably twofold. Potassium ions appear to replace magnesium within the particle. The further effect of potassium which cannot be suppressed by addition of magnesium is probably due to ionic effects upon charged groups. An additional complication sets in when the particles are exposed to potassium chloride solution at room temperature. As will be described in more detail later, the RNA in the dissociated particles is now hydrolyzed by the contaminating RNAase in the preparation with a rate eight times higher than the rate constant for attack of the RNA of the nondissociated particles. The effect of the contaminating RNAase on the particles in 0.7 *M* KCl can be observed by comparing figures 4*a* and 4*b*. There is much more material of very low sedimentation coefficient in the room-temperature runs. Furthermore, the area ratio of the 80 S : 60 S : 40 S components in the low-temperature run is 1.3 : 1.8 : 1.0, whereas in the run affected by RNAase it is about 1 : 1 : 3. The 40 S component, therefore, may be more resistant to RNAase than the others.

Magnesium ions can be further removed by EDTA. At neutral *p*H, the system treated with EDTA aggregates at room temperature. Thus, this system can be analyzed only at low temperature or at alkaline *p*H. In *p*H 6.5 phosphate buffer, and in the presence of 2.5×10^{-2} *M* EDTA, the particles dissociate to yield components of 40 S (64 per cent), 26 S (30 per cent) and 3 to 6 S (6 per cent) (fig. 5*b*). Lower concentrations of versene, such as 5×10^{-3} *M*, yielded poor resolution of the 40 and 26 S components (fig. 5*a*). At higher *p*H (9.0), higher concentrations of EDTA (5×10^{-2} *M*), and room temperature, the particles dissociate into the 40 and 26 S units together with increased amounts of material of 3 to 6 S(fig. 5*c*). Dialysis to remove EDTA and to replenish magnesium causes aggregation of the system. It should be noted

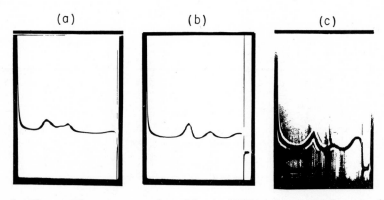

Fig. 5. Ultracentrifuge patterns of particles in EDTA. Speed 42,040 rpm. (*a*) In 5×10^{-3} *M* EDTA, *p*H 6.6, 0.025 μ K-PO$_4$ 0° C, for 1 hour. Centrifuged at 4.6–6.0° C. (*b*) In 2.5×10^{-2} *M* EDTA, *p*H 6.6, 0.025 μ K-PO$_4$, 0° C, for 1 hour. Centrifuged at 6° C. (*c*) In 5×10^{-2} *M* EDTA, *p*H 9.0, 0.02 *M* K-CO$_3$, 0° C, for 3 hours. Centrifuged at 20°C.

that in this concentration of versene (0.05 *M*), and at *p*H 9.0, less than 1 per cent of the original magnesium should remain with the particles.

The RNA/protein ratios of the dissociated components have been investigated. The 60 and 40 S components were shown to be attacked and precipitated by RNAase and protamine, indicating that they contain RNA. The problem was then approached more quantitatively by comparing the ultracentrifuge patterns obtained by schlieren optics with those obtained by ultraviolet absorption optics which measures the sedimentation of nucleic acid. It should be noted that the concentration of particles in solutions employed for ultraviolet absorption optics is 30 to 50 times lower than that used for schlieren optics. In dilute solutions, the sedimentation coefficient will be higher and the reversible dissociation reaction will proceed further toward completion. Figure 6*a* shows that all the nucleic acid moves as one component of 79 S in water. At *p*H 7.5, 0.05 μ, phosphate (fig. 6*b*), the particles are dissociated into two ultraviolet-absorbing components of 37 and 59 S, those shown above to appear also in the schlieren pattern. The absence of the 80 S particles, which do appear in the schlieren pattern, in the ultraviolet absorption pattern in this phosphate buffer is to be attributed to the complete dissociation of the original particles

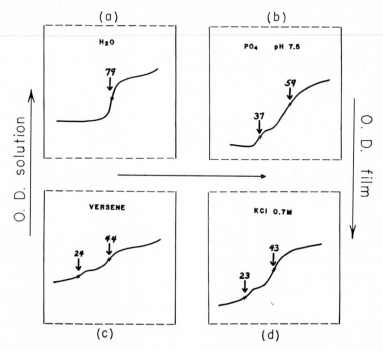

Fig. 6. Ultracentrifuge ultraviolet absorption patterns of particles under dissociating and nondissociating conditions. (*a*) In water. Rotor speed 25, 980 rpm. (*b*) In 0.05 μ K-PO$_4$, *p*H 7.5, 0° C, for 1 hour. Centrifuged at 7.7° C. Rotor speed 37,020 rpm. (*c*) In 0.025 *M* ETDA, *p*H 6.6, 0.025 μ, K-PO$_4$, 0° C, for 1 hour. Centrifuged at 6.2° C. Rotor speed 42,040 rpm. (*d*) In 0.7 *M* KCl, 0° C, for 1 hour. Centrifuged at 8.5° C. Rotor speed 37,020 rpm.

into the 59 and 39 S components at the low concentration. The ratio of the amounts of ultraviolet-absorbing material, i.e., nucleic acid, contained in the 59 and 39 S boundaries is similar to the ratio of amounts of material contained in the two boundaries as observed with schlieren optics. These ratios are approximately 2.3 : 1. Treatment with EDTA results in nucleic acid–containing components of 24 and 44 S (fig. 6c) as were likewise observed by schlieren optics (fig. 5b). The ratio of the amounts of nucleic acid in the two components is similar to the ratio of the amounts of material contained in the two boundaries as observed in schlieren optics, namely, 2 : 1. The pattern of the particles incubated in 0.7 *M* KCl and observed with absorption optics (fig. 6d) is, however, markedly different from that observed with schlieren optics (fig. 4b). Components of 75 and 58 S which are observed with schlieren optics are not observed with absorption optics. In the latter case, however, a new boundary of component 23 S is present to the extent of about 40 per cent of the 43 S component. The probable explanation of this behavior is that, at the low concentration necessary for the employment of ultraviolet optics, the 80 S and the 59 S particles are further dissociated to an undetectable concentration and a new component of lower sedimentation appears. The 24 S component observed with ultraviolet optics in potassium chloride–treated preparations is presumably similar to or identical with the 25 S component observed in solutions treated with EDTA. Thus, the original particles and their dissociation products all have similar ratios of ultraviolet-absorbing material to mass.

The intrinsic viscosity of microsomal particles in media which promote dissociation was studied in order to find out what over-all changes in frictional coefficient are attendant upon dissociation. These experiments were performed in versene and in potassium chloride solutions at low temperature since at higher temperature the system in versene aggregates and the system in potassium chloride shows evidence of ribonuclease action. Even though particle preparations were clarified twice by low-speed centrifugation, the possibility of the presence of small amounts of aggregates cannot be excluded. The intrinsic viscosity of the microsomal particles in phosphate buffer was found to be 0.11 (100 cc/g) (fig. 7a), identical with the value found for 24° C. In water, the value was 0.12/100 cc/g, an increase which may be due to the electroviscous effect. In solutions of dissociated particles in versene at *p*H 6.8 and 9.0, and in potassium chloride (fig. 7b, c, d), a slightly higher value of reduced viscosity was obtained at high concentration. The intrinsic viscosity of these solutions, however, was again found to be 0.11 to 0.12. Thus, no change in intrinsic viscosity is observed upon dissociation of the particles. The most reasonable explanation for this result is that the units of 60, 40, and 25 S have the same frictional coefficient as the 80 S particles.

The above experiments on the dissociation of the 80 S particles can be summarized as follows:

1. When magnesium and calcium are removed from microsomal particles (79 to 81 S), three ultracentrifugally identifiable components are obtained as

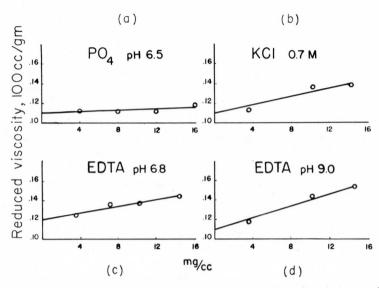

Fig. 7. Reduced viscosity of particles under dissociating and nondissociating conditions. (*a*) In 0.025 μ PO₄, *p*H 6.5, with 1 × 10⁻⁴ *M* MgCl₂. (*b*) In 0.7 *M* KCl, *p*H 6.5, 0.02 μ K-PO₄, 0° C, for 3 hours. (*c*) In 0.03 *M* EDTA, *p*H 6.8, 0.02 μ K-PO₄, 0° C, for 3 hours. (*d*) In 0.05 *M* EDTA, *p*H 9.0, 0.01 *M* Tris buffer, 0° C, for 3 hours.

dissociation products. At infinite dilution these components have sedimentation coefficients of 59 to 61 S, 40 to 43 S, and 25 to 27 S.

2. All these units contain nucleic acid and probably have RNA/protein ratios similar to that of the 80 S particles.

3. The mixtures, and perhaps the individual units, of 60, 40, and 25 S components have frictional coefficients similar to that of the 80 S particles.

4. Under conditions in which only 60 and 40 S units are formed by dissociation of 80 S particles, the two components occur in an amount ratio of 2.2–2.3 to 1 respectively in both schlieren and absorption optics. Treatment with EDTA over a wide range of concentration of both EDTA and particles results in the formation of only 40 and 25 S units. These are present in an amount ratio of 2:1, indicating that the two units in the system are in a stable state.

On the basis of the above observations, the molecular weights of the 60, 40, and 25 S components can be estimated to be 2.6 to 3.0×10⁶, 1.3 to 1.5×10⁶, and 6.5 to 7.5×10⁵, respectively. The ratios between the molecular weight of the 80 S particles and the molecular weights of the successively smaller units are then in the series 6:4:2:1. Chao has reached a similar conclusion for the 60 and 40 S components of yeast particles [4]. Reports of Wagman, and of Tissieres and Watson, in this meeting also tend to support this formulation. Both groups find that the 40 S particle from *Escherichia coli* is spherical, with an RNA/protein ratio close to unity, and a molecular weight of 1.3 to 1.8 million. Since the 40 S particle is spherical, the difference between its sedimentation coefficient and the sedimentation coefficients of the 60 and 80 S particles of *E. coli* reported by Bolton et al. in this meeting is most probably due to differences in molecular weight. These would then form the series 3 : 2 :1. In addition, particles of 25 S have been found as dissociation products of the 40 S particle of *E. coli* by Tissieres and Watson, this too having a spherical shape in the electron microscope, as observed by Hall. A 25 S component has also been reported by Chao [4] as one of the dissociation products of yeast particles.

The following scheme is proposed to account for the experimental findings concerned with the dissociation of the 80 S particles. When a certain fraction of the magnesium ion is removed from the system (about 50 per cent as based on the binding constants of RNA and phosphate [5]), the 80 S particle dissociates reversibly to form a 40 S unit, one-third of the original particle, and a 60 S unit, two-thirds of the original particle. When larger amounts of magnesium ions are removed (over 95 per cent, by versene), not only does dissociation of the 80 S particles to 40 and 60 S units occur, but in addition the 60 S unit also is degraded, possibly irreversibly, to form a 40 S unit and two 25 S units. The final result of such a dissociation should be a system containing two 40 S units and two 25 S units per original 80 S particle. This formulation, then, fits the experimental findings both as to the mass ratio of 2:1 between 40 and 60 S units and as to the mass ratio of 2:1 between 40 and 25 S components.

The magnesium and calcium contents of the particle have been analyzed by flame spectrophotometry.[2] There are 3.0 to 3.2 μmoles of magnesium per 12 μmoles of RNA-phosphorus or per 10 mg dry weight of particles. All the magnesium appears to be extractable by 0.5 N TCA at $0°$ C. Assuming that calcium can also be completely extracted by TCA, then, again, per 12 μmoles of RNA-phosphorus, there is 0.45 to 0.55 μmole of calcium, about one-sixth of the amount of magnesium. Thus, the particles contain 3.5 to 3.7 μmoles of magnesium and calcium per 12 μmoles of phosphate, or 1 mole of divalent ions for each 3.3 ± 0.2 μmoles of phosphate.

It is of interest to estimate the apportionment of these divalent ions between the RNA and the protein. Combining the data on molecular weight (4.5×10^6), RNA content (40 per cent), and content of divalent ions per mole of phosphorus, we may calculate that there are 1.5×10^3 moles of magnesium and calcium per mole of particle. Since the cation binding capacity of the microsomal protein is unknown, we introduce for comparison the results that may be calculated for bovine serum albumin, a protein with a high proportion of dicarboxylic amino acids. According to Carr [6], there are 8 calcium binding sites per molecule at pH 7.4. The total amount of protein per mole of microsomal particles is equivalent to 36 moles of bovine serum albumin. This protein would therefore bind no more than 300 moles of calcium, and would account for less than 20 per cent of the divalent ions bound by the particles. We con-

[2] The technical assistance of Mr. Merck Robison, Carnation Company, is gratefully acknowledged.

clude, therefore, that more than 80 per cent of the divalent ions are bound by RNA. Experiments with pancreatic ribonuclease further support this conclusion. By the action of ribonuclease, a partial separation of protein and degraded nucleic acid of the particles is achieved. Most of the protein precipitates from solution, leaving behind a mixture of nucleotides and polynucleotides. The distribution of magnesium between supernatant and precipitate should provide information concerning the binding sites of the magnesium ions. It was found that, after RNAase had acted on the particles for 2 hours, 85 per cent of the magnesium had been liberated into the supernatant, which contains 65 per cent of the nucleotide phosphate and only 10 to 15 per cent of the protein. If we assume that 80 per cent of the magnesium is associated with RNA in the particle, then half of the phosphate groups in the RNA exist in the form of magnesium salts.

Attempts to study the protein of the particle have been made with RNAase. After 3 hours' incubation with 7 µg/ml of pancreatic RNAase in a 1 per cent solution of particles at 27° C, the solution becomes turbid. Between 85 and 90 per cent of the total protein and 8 per cent of the total phosphorus are sedimentable by low-speed centrifugation, leaving 10 to 15 per cent of the protein and 90 per cent of the phosphorus in the form of mono- or oligonucleotides in the supernatant. That the protein aggregation is related to RNAase action and not to the presence of nucleotides was shown by experiments in which large amounts of 2,3′-phosphate nucleotides were added to particle preparations without aggregating effect. The protein aggregate is insoluble in buffer at pH 4 to 11, in strong salt solution, in acid, in urea, or in performic acid, but does dissolve in alkali at pH 12 to 13 as well as in 80 per cent saturated guanidium chloride at pH 8 to 9. If the guanidium ions are removed by dialysis or if the pH is lowered to 10 to 11, the protein again precipitates.

The action of RNAase on the particles is enhanced by addition of potassium chloride or phosphate buffer and is suppressed by addition of magnesium. It was also found that there is a small amount of contaminating RNAase in our preparation of particles. Incubation of particles in phosphate buffer (0.05 µ, pH 6.5) for only 2 hours at room temperature hydrolyzes 4 to 5 per cent of the RNA. This rate can be increased by 8 times by addition of potassium chloride (0.15 to 0.7 M), and it can be suppressed back to 1.5 to 2 times by addition of magnesium chloride (0.001 M) with the potassium chloride.

The present studies shed little light on the nature of the binding between RNA and protein. Electrostatic forces cannot be the only ones involved, since at least half of the phosphate groups of the RNA are present in the form of salt linkages with magnesium and calcium. In addition, RNA does not separate from protein in the ultracentrifuge in the presence of 0.7 to 1.0 M KCl, nor can protein be separated from nucleic acid by alcohol precipitation in such solutions. Agents which denature proteins, such as phenol or detergent, have been successfully applied to separate RNA from the protein of the particle. The protein, however, aggregates as the RNA is removed, as shown by the experiment with RNAase. These findings, coupled with the fact that urea does demolish the particle, suggest that hydrogen bonding between RNA and protein may be an important factor in holding the two constituents together.

Microsomal particles have been isolated from sections of pea seedlings that have been incubated with C^{14}-leucine for 1 hour.[3] The particles, after a series of centrifugations and dialyses, were shown to be void of contaminating free C^{14}-leucine, by two methods. The specific activity (cpm/mg protein) of such particles was the same as that of particles which were washed further by hot TCA and 1 N NaOH. Moreover, acid hydrolysis of the microsomal protein after treatment with dinitrofluorobenzene yields over 98 per cent of the C^{14}-leucine as free leucine, indicating that most of the C^{14}-leucine is linked inside the protein molecule. With such a preparation of labeled 80 S particles, we wish to find answers to two specific questions.

The first question is based on the idea that only about 1 to 5 per cent [7] of the protein in the particle is being actively synthesized in the particles. It has been suggested that this newly formed protein then passes into the cytoplasm. In the dissociation studies, it is found that after treatment with EDTA, pH 6.5, most of the nucleoproteins aggregate and sediment out of solution, leaving about 6 per cent of protein in the supernatant. After the action of RNAase, there is also about 10 per cent of protein which stays in the solution with the nucleotides, while 90 per cent of the protein precipitates out of solution. When the labeled particles were subjected to the above two treatments, only a small percentage of the total counts of the labeled protein remained in the supernatant, while over 90 per cent of the counts precipitated with the aggregates. The supernatant proteins obtained from these two treatments were precipitated by TCA and were shown to have specific activities no higher than that of the aggregated nucleoproteins. This experiment suggests that substantial removal of magnesium and RNA does not liberate a large percentage of labeled proteins or proteins of very high specific activity from the isolated particles.

The second question is based on the idea that RNA is a template [8]. Thus, is there a large amount of radioactive amino acids in the particle attached to RNA through covalent bonds? The RNA was separated from protein by phenol as well as by density gradient centrifugation in cesium chloride. Invariably, very few if any counts could be found in the RNA. Furthermore, the soluble nucleotide fraction of the supernatant after deproteinization by TCA, obtained by RNAase treatment of the particles, also contained very few counts. Therefore, if amino acids are attached to RNA through covalent bonds, the total amount of such material at a given time is likely to be very small.

In summary, microsomal particles from pea seedlings consist of smaller units of nucleoproteins cemented together through linkage of magnesium ions and the phosphate group of RNA. RNA and the protein(s) in these units are held

---

[3] Experiments with C^{14}-amino acids were performed in cooperation with Dr. Clifford Sato.

tightly together, probably through hydrogen bonds. Removal of magnesium ions and hydrolysis of RNA from the particles labeled with C^{14}-amino acids in the cell did not liberate labeled amino acid or protein(s) of high specific activity from the particles.

REFERENCES

1. P. O. P. Ts'o, J. Bonner, and J. Vinograd, *J. Biophys. Biochem. Cytol., 2,* 451 (1956).

2. Fu-Chaun Chao and H. K. Schachman, *Arch. Biochem. Biophys., 61,* 220 (1956).

3. M. E. Petermann and M. G. Hamilton, *J. Biol. Chem., 224,* 725 (1957).

4. Fu-Chaun Chao, *Arch. Biochem. Biophys., 70,* 426 (1957).

5. J. S. Wieberg and W. F. Neuman, *Arch. Biochem. Biophys., 72,* 66 (1957).

6. C. W. Carr, *Arch. Biochem. Biophys., 43,* 147 (1953).

7. J. W. Littlefield, E. B. Keller, J. Gross, and P. C. Zamecnik, *J. Biol. Chem., 217,* 111 (1955).

8. H. Borsook, *J. Cellular Comp. Physiol., 47,* Supplement 1, 35 (1956).